Effective
Food Hygiene
TRAINING

A guide for owners and managers of food businesses,
enforcement officers, trainers and potential trainers

Euan M.R. MacAuslan
FRSH, FRIPH, FITOL, MCIPD, MIIRSM

PUBLISHED BY
© HIGHFIELD.CO.UK LTD

'Vue Pointe', Spinney Hill, Sprotbrough,
Doncaster, DN5 7LY, UK
Tel: +44 0845 2260350
Facsimile: +44 0845 2260360
E-mail: richard@highfield.co.uk

Websites:
www.highfield.co.uk
www.foodsafetytrainers.co.uk

ISBN 1 904 544 134

Dedication
I would like to dedicate this book to Katie, Isobel and Louise.

First published 2003

© **HIGHFIELD.CO.UK.LTD**

ISBN 1 904 544 134

Printed by Apple Tree Print • Telephone: 01302 314011

Contents

Foreword by Richard A. Sprenger

Many people believe that food poisoning can be reduced by sending all food handlers on accredited courses. This belief stems from the mistaken view that ignorance causes food poisoning and therefore the provision of knowledge and an understanding of the consequences of poor hygiene will result in higher standards of food safety.

Unfortunately, it is the failure to implement good practice which is the main cause of food poisoning and this is primarily a result of poor management and inadequate supervision.

To be effective, food safety training must be relevant to the duties of the food handler and should only be provided after a comprehensive training needs analysis. Having determined the knowledge and skills necessary for a particular food handler the analysis will ascertain the existing levels of skills and knowledge. The difference between what is currently known and the knowledge and skills required will form the basis of the training.

However, research and experience suggests that even when the requisite knowledge is provided there are often too many barriers to the implementation of this knowledge. This is particularly the case with remote classroom based generic food safety courses if staff are not motivated to implement their newly acquired knowledge.

Other barriers commonly encountered include lack of time, lack of facilities, a failure to understand, especially when the food handler does not speak English, poor management and an unacceptable culture which penalizes good hygiene instead of rewarding it.

It is essential, therefore, that organisations appreciate there is much more to training than sending food handlers on the first available accredited course. Although there are many excellent reasons for food handlers, especially supervisors and managers, obtaining food safety qualifications, good hygiene practice and the law requires competency not certification.

Successful training will be based on an effective training programme that usually starts with management and supervisors and will include induction, awareness, reinforcement and continuous refresher training of food handlers through effective supervision. Organisations which train and motivate managers and supervisors are much more likely to develop a culture of food safety which encourages newly trained staff to implement good practice.

Continuous refresher training of food handlers is essential to ensure competencies are maintained. Cost-effective refresher training of food handlers is best carried out on-site by well-trained supervisors but knowledge may also be provided by using comprehensive interactive computer based programs.

This book provides a wealth of information which should assist most trainers to improve the effectiveness of their training. I hope you find it as interesting and enjoyable as I did.

Preface

Training food handlers in the hospitality and retail food industries has been recommended by various organisations as a means of improving food safety practices and food safety for consumers. There is a statutory requirement to ensure that food handlers receive adequate supervision and instruction and/or training in food safety matters commensurate with their work activity. However, food hygiene training does not just affect food hygiene practices or help businesses comply with legislation. Training may contribute to a Defence of Due Diligence if properly managed. It also motivates employees, helps with career development, and can contribute to the development of a food safety culture within the business. Proprietors of food businesses (especially small independently run businesses) all too often neglect employee training and development for a range of reasons such as a lack of resources, staff turnover, and an ignorance of suitable available training.

It is over 20 years since the first basic food hygiene certificate level examinations were made available to food handlers in the UK. Since then little has changed in the syllabuses and the way the multiple choice questions are worded. Over six million food hygiene certificates have been awarded. The Food Standards Agency estimate (without any real scientific evidence) that over one million people each year have food poisoning in the UK. In addition, the range of languages spoken by food handlers working in the UK has increased substantially since more employers are recruiting those who speak English as a second language. Training can be an unwelcome expense for managers where there is a high turnover of employees, especially amongst those for whom English is not their first language. During the mid 1980s food hygiene education disappeared from the schools' curriculum. Now changes are in place to bring it back into schools. To improve practical implementation of food hygiene theory it is time to develop a radical strategy concerning the way training *and* education are targeted and delivered in the United Kingdom, and perhaps Europe.

This book seeks to provide a guide to food hygiene training for anyone concerned with training, including owners of food businesses, managers, supervisors, trainers and enforcement officers. To use this book alone to improve food safety training standards would be misguided. It intentionally leaves out in-depth reasoning and explanation.

The reader is strongly advised to: read publications about food safety and training of food handlers; make use of food hygiene conferences and papers; talk to colleagues in the industry; seek advice from Environmental Health Officers (EHO); use the internet; and consult a range of organisations or industry bodies for more information and advice.

Euan MacAuslan

Acknowledgements

I would like to thank the following for providing me with the inspiration and advice in helping me to produce this book: Richard Sprenger from Highfield.co.uk Limited, Richard Taylor from Creative Learning Media, Eunice Taylor from Salford University, Denise Worsfold from UWIC, Graham Aston from Eaton Publications, the editorial team of The Royal Society for the Promotion of Health, Dr Richard North, HMSO, the Councillors and officers of The Royal Borough of Kensington and Chelsea. Various employees from the Food Standards Agency, Institute of Food Science and Technology, Hospitality Training Foundation, Support Training and Services plc, and Restaurant Association have also provided invaluable information and enlightenment. Also, thanks are due to the Royal Army Medical Corps who gave me my first posting, after initial training as an Environmental Health Assistant, to the former School of Army Health as an instructor between 1978 and 1982 where my interest in training was fertilised. The thousands of trainees who have been (patiently) on the receiving end of my good and bad training techniques are not to be forgotten. Any omissions of individuals and organisations that have helped me through my career to reach this point are purely accidental.

Every effort to obtain permission to reproduce material in this book has been made from the appropriate source. Any errors or omissions will be rectified in future reprints, provided the publisher is contacted.

The view and opinions expressed in this book are entirely those of the author and not of the Royal Borough of Kensington and Chelsea.

Introduction

Are you seeking clarification about food hygiene training? What does it have to do with your business, employees and customers? What is the activity in your business: food production, food wholesale, retail food, hospitality, hotel, restaurant, café, leisure, healthcare, residential care, childcare, educational, voluntary, charity, H.M. Forces, etc? There will be employees in all these, and other food businesses, who will need some form of food hygiene training. What will Environmental Health Officers from local authorities want to know about food hygiene training in your premises? Are you currently a trainer, or thinking about becoming a trainer? Or, are you an enforcement officer who needs to know more about food hygiene training, instruction and supervision before giving advice to or serving a notice on a food business proprietor?

Training is a complex issue. Some people seem gifted in training. Others need to be taught how to train. Often training can become an enjoyable and rewarding skill, especially when people learn and achieve through behavioural change. Training is a structured process in which the following factors must be taken into account:
   ♦   determination of the training need;
   ♦   planning the training;
   ♦   delivery of training;
   ♦   implementation of the training upon return to the workplace; and
   ♦   post-training evaluation to assess the impact upon the organisation and the recipient.

Before reading on, you may wish to consider that:
   ♦   an understanding of food safety legislation is not enough to prevent food poisoning;
   ♦   food poisoning is preventable if the principles of hazard analysis and other food safety management systems are used;
   ♦   food safety measures and food hygiene practice are not entirely the responsibility of the food retail and hospitality industries – poor food hygiene practice in the home may equally be to blame for recent rises in food poisoning incidents;
   ♦   a change in an individual's food hygiene practice may benefit their family, friends, colleagues and their employer's business. However, food handlers with good domestic food hygiene practices are more likely to bring good standards into work if their managers and supervisors motivate, encourage and involve them in a food safety culture;
   ♦   it is a catalogue of errors which contribute to food poisoning. Certificates alone do not prevent food poisoning;
   ♦   food poisoning does not happen every day. The food and hospitality industries in general do a good job – but there is always room for improvement and for removing any complacency;
   ♦   once a food handler receives a nationally recognised food hygiene certificate or any other type of food hygiene training they and their employer will have to demonstrate practical implementation of the theory taught, and provide suitable evidence of refresher training. This type of training should be continuous, especially on-the-job. This will be proved through competency assessment through effective supervision.

Holding a certificate may lead to a false sense of security;
♦ competency rather than certification is the way forward; and
♦ above all, training is a continuous process which requires effective supervision.

Please note that this book is intended an introduction to the world of food hygiene training for managers of both small and large businesses, enforcement officers, trainers and those thinking about becoming trainers. For ease of reading technical and academic detail have, where possible, been omitted. Readers are strongly advised to consult the last pages of each chapter where they will find further reading suggestions. Appendix I has a list of useful contacts.

Before moving on consider the following:

> If, of all words of tongue and pen,
> The saddest are, "It might have been,"
> More sad are these we daily see:
> "It is, but hadn't ought to be!"
>
> Bret Harte (1839-1902)

…in other words, if you cannot train someone to be competent in the job they do and be able to demonstrate good food hygiene practice, do not do it at all!

1 Competency or Certification?

"Whatsoever one would understand what he hears must hasten to put into practice what he has heard." (St Gregory the Great, 6th Century)

What's it called...?

What is the correct title of the accredited Foundation food hygiene certificate in the UK? Take your pick:

- ◆ Certificate in Health & Hygiene;
- ◆ EHO Food Health Certificate;
- ◆ EHO Basic Foundation Hygiene Certificate;
- ◆ Hygiene and Health Certificate;
- ◆ Health and Hygiene Certificate;
- ◆ Health and Food Certificate;
- ◆ Food and Hygiene Certificate;
- ◆ Food Handling Certificate;
- ◆ Basic Foundation Hygiene and Safety Certificate; and
- ◆ Food Hygiene Certificate to open a business.

On second thoughts, none of these is correct. It should read: Foundation Certificate in Food Hygiene. The Qualifications and Curriculum Authority (QCA) accredits examinations run by bodies such as The Chartered Institute of Environmental Health (CIEH), The Royal Society for the Promotion of Health (RSPH), The Royal Institute of Public Health (RIPH) and the Royal Environmental Health Institute of Scotland (REHIS). The list above shows examples of some common names which have been given by managers and food handlers who are trying to book themselves on to courses and do not really understand what they are asking for. If courses were run in-house and unaccredited then the organisers would be perfectly entitled to give the courses whatever title they liked.

Certificates are required – aren't they?

Consider the following situation:

An interviewee for a new job, within a food business, turns up for an interview. Key points which the interviewer looks for are experience, attitude, personal cleanliness and appearance. The interviewer also asks to see evidence of food hygiene certificates. Is this because the interviewer thinks it is a legal requirement to hold a certificate in food hygiene, or is it because the interviewer thinks that a certificate is evidence of competency? The interviewer fails to ask the interviewee about any food hygiene theory to test current knowledge, nor does the interviewer assess any practical application of food hygiene theory by the interviewee. Perhaps the interviewer does not feel competent to ask about (or even assess) any issues regarding food hygiene.

Before reading further, therefore, consider for a moment – which is more important: possession of a certificate or a demonstration of competency?

The quotations below have been taken from conversations had with the author by managers who have tried to book places on courses that he has been responsible for organising over the last decade:

♦ "Expiry date on a certificate is imminent."
♦ "The certificate runs out after two years."
♦ "It is a legal requirement to hold a food hygiene certificate."
♦ "Managers only have to take a Foundation Certificate in Food Hygiene."
♦ "If someone fails their certificate they cannot work as a food handler."

The problem with the above is that they are commonly encountered by trainers and EHOs who understand what the legal training requirement is all about. None of these statements is true. They are all misconceptions which need to be addressed nationally so that the industry and enforcement agencies speak the same language. Another place that incorrect quotes appear are in catering job advertisements, such as:

♦ to comply with EHO regulations;
♦ to meet EHO's Food Safety laws;
♦ applicants must hold a current health & hygiene certificate;
♦ executive chefs must have at least a Foundation Certificate in Food Hygiene; and
♦ food handling certificates are desirable.

First of all, EHOs do not make the regulations or legislation. That is Parliament's responsibility. What do employers mean by "current" certificate – and why not give it the correct name? An executive chef with just a foundation certificate who wants to move into a management position has obviously never received any training in hygiene management. At interviews it is rare for employers in small businesses to test current hygiene knowledge of interviewees – is this because they have not had training themselves?

Unfortunately, even local authority enforcement officers even get the words "certification" and "competency" muddled up. Some incorrectly interpret the legislation and codes of practice by wording improvement notices to read "food handlers must be trained and acquire certificates in food hygiene", rather than saying "food handlers must receive training commensurate with their work activity". This is usually due to ignorance and a lack of understanding of both legal interpretation and what is actually in the interests of public health and the food business. For enforcement officers there may be a conflict of interest between their role as enforcers and educators. However, amendments in Codes of Practice under the Food Safety Act 1990, and pending changes in legislation controlling the way local authorities operate will certainly provide enforcement officers with clearer guidance.

Scenes from the high street

The examples below illustrate situations which enforcement agencies and businesses have encountered without really considering if either competency and/or certification are more important:

♦ An EHO walks into a café to carry out a routine inspection. A Foundation Certificate in Food Hygiene is displayed on the wall for the customers to see. The EHO asks the manager if she may see the employee whose name is on the certificate. They reply was that the employee had left two years ago. The certificate is now a meaningless bit of paper.

- Two butchers' shops in the same urban street. One butcher has obtained his licence as required by the Food Safety (General Food Hygiene) (Butchers' Shops) Amendment Regulations 2000. Licences are required for premises where open raw meat and ready to eat foods are sold. He attended various Meat and Livestock Commission courses. The butcher now has qualifications in HACCP(hazard analysis and critical control point) and an Intermediate Certificate in Food Hygiene. The other butcher has not been granted his licence. He has not passed his examinations because he is dyslexic. Despite there being no legal requirement to hold a certificate the latter butcher has the considerably better standards of hygiene. This poses a dilemma for the local authority. In terms of competency it is better to demonstrate practical application of knowledge, rather than learning the theory to meet a legal obligation.

- The manager of a major residential care home asked a local authority to provide food hygiene refresher training for her sixty staff. They had all attended the Foundation Certificate in Food Hygiene course sometime over the last two years. The refresher course was to last for two hours and a certificate of attendance was to be issued. No one would admit responsibility for temperature monitoring, segregation of cleaning materials, handwashing policies, or check incoming food supplies. For the residential home manager certificates seemed the key issue. Refresher training should be continuous.

- An EHO served an Improvement Notice on a café owner to provide food hygiene training for his employees. The notice stated that employees were to receive training to an equivalent level of basic food hygiene certificate. All the EHO was interested in was that the employees passed their certificate examination so that she could say that the notice had been complied with.

- A large restaurant has arranged for all its employees to go on a certificate course in English. The problem is that the staff speak a range of languages and the manager has difficulty in communicating with all of them. She assumes that the training is necessary because that is what the law states.

- Staff return from a course full of good intent to make good their previously bad food hygiene practices. The trouble is there is a new manager who does not like "timewasters" including staff who are diligent about washing hands properly and frequently. The manager is satisfied that to meet the legal requirement staff have a certificate – never mind what they get up to in the business.

- In this last example, a number of food handlers in the business have received on-the-job training. The owner sees no reason to put them on certificate courses. Morale is good, supervision and instruction are good, as well as a more than satisfactory risk rating given by the local EHO. A high level of competency has been achieved without any classroom-based training.

The following example is described in a bit more detail. Imagine a café in Central London. The owner is running his other branch about a mile away. He is at the latter because the local authority EHO had served various improvement notices for hazard analysis and improper labelling of food. The manager's attitude was that "I only have to do something towards improving food hygiene when the EHO tells me to. It's her problem not mine!" The manager deemed himself to be competent in food hygiene because he had attended a basic food hygiene certificate in 1990 but had not undertaken any refresher training or informed his staff about what they should do. Back to the first branch in Central London. Here, one morning, the local authority enforcement officer walked in – not on duty – but to have a coffee and lunch break. He sat himself at the front of the café near a state-of-the-art chill display unit. An integral part of the unit was a marble chopping board. Being nosey, as officers can be, he looked at the plastic chopping boards on the marble board. On the sides of these boards was stamped "raw meat only". On the boards were unwrapped alternating plates of some turkey and smoked salmon. Not horizontally – but vertically! To one side a girl was preparing baguettes for the lunch time service. She cut her finger with the buttering knife. After licking her wound she proceeded with her work. No plaster or handwashing here. A buzzer went. A man who was using a feed-slicer was collecting the sliced turkey in his bare hand. Closer inspection of the underside of the slicer revealed a rainbow of different congealed foodstuffs. Anyway, on hearing the buzzer the man wiped his hands on his t-shirt, opened the oven door, and because the rolls were hot he spat on his fingers before taking the rolls out the oven. Not surprisingly the enforcement officer decided against ordering his meal, and instead asked a colleague to visit the café with a camera for collecting photographic evidence, bringing the owner along with him. The owner, on questioning, replied "It is your job to tell me what to do. I have my *certificate*, and I have *competence* in my staff!" (A Freudian slip no doubt!)

Proceed with caution...

Good News! Holding a Foundation Certificate in Food Hygiene (formerly Basic Food Hygiene [or equivalent level] certificate), or higher level, is GOOD for a business. The course provides underpinning knowledge of food hygiene. BUT! The proprietor and trainee must turn the theory into *practice*.

Once a candidate has attended a certificate course the proprietor will have to provide evidence of continuous training and how they have been instructed in food hygiene matters relevant to the work activity. The *Hazard Analysis* for the business premises will highlight the need for further training. The course content should be relevant to the business and not generic.

Training produces learning and understanding, plus the practical application of the theory taught on courses. Certificate courses do provide good evidence of nationally recognised theoretical knowledge, help motivate staff, assist with career prospects, and set a minimum standard of understanding. Practice of that knowledge will have to be encouraged and instruction will have to be provided by the proprietor. Proprietors have a duty to ensure that all training (including refresher and certificate courses) is commensurate with a food handler's work activity. For instance, if they are a supervisor or manager, they would benefit from Intermediate or Advanced training - followed by regular refresher and practical food hygiene training. A word of advice: a manager cannot supervise a food handler if they themselves have not received a higher level of training. The burden of responsibility cannot be passed on to an external trainer.

Ensure that training given is satisfactory. Make sure that it is consistent, relevant, continuous, up-to-date and understandable. It will help change behaviour and help individuals focus on their jobs. Effective training will help in the implementation of hazard analysis. Training records, if kept, must be up-to-date. Written records are not a legal requirement but they may help with a due diligence defence. Although there is no legal requirement to hold a nationally recognised basic, intermediate or advanced certificate in food hygiene, these are considered, by some, to be best because they show evidence of theoretical training. However, the examination questions for the accredited course may have no connection with the work carried out by a food handler who attended the course, for example, a question about the storage of fish in a fridge, when the food handler works in a hand made chocolate production business, or is a night-time baker in a supermarket store. There is no expiry date on accredited certificates BUT proprietors should be able to demonstrate suitable on-going supervision and refresher training for themselves and each of their food handlers. Others would argue that all training must be suitable for the needs of the individual and the business. As long as systems work effectively, and staff are competent, certificates may be irrelevant to the management of food hygiene within a business.

Do not let yourself fall into traps
♦ in the wrong hands holding a certificate can provide a false sense of security and may be no defence of due diligence. Managers and food handlers will have to show evidence of turning the theory taught on food hygiene courses into practice;
♦ the Foundation Certificate in Food Hygiene does not provide evidence of competency or practical application; and
♦ repeatedly sending candidates on the same level food hygiene certificate courses for refresher training is misguided and does not demonstrate an understanding of practical implementation. Proper relevant *update* courses or attending a *higher level* course, in addition to practical supervision, would be more beneficial.

SO WHAT ARE COMPETENCY AND CERTIFICATION?

COMPETENCY:
A competency is an underlying characteristic of a person which enables them to deliver superior performance in a given job, role or situation. It is those characteristics which distinguish the "best" from the average. A competent person is someone who can satisfy the requirements of knowledge, skills, and attitudes that are needed to carry out a specific activity. For instance a food handler may be deemed competent if s/he understands why accurate temperature recording is important, in addition to:
♦ practically carrying out temperature recording be a pre-determined method;
♦ being in receipt of practical training and supervision in temperature recording; and
♦ knowing what to do if the temperatures fall outside the requirements for a specific process.

Competency is not just about being in possession of a food hygiene certificate. Someone may have failed an accredited examination, but they can still store food correctly in a fridge, or know what to do if a cockroach is seen in their premises. This does not make them incompetent to do their job…does it? To help the individual, further training, coaching and development will be required. Repeatedly sending someone on a Foundation Certificate in Food Hygiene because they failed the previous examination or because they need refresher training will not make them competent.

CERTIFICATION:

A certificate is a written declaration of attainment or achievement, for example a nationally recognised food hygiene certificate such as an Intermediate Certificate in Food Hygiene (now called Intermediate Certificate in Food Safety). It could also be a company specific certificate of attendance, such as "attendance at Sam 'n' Ella's one-day course on Assured Safe Catering". On its own it does not demonstrate that the food handler is competent. He or she may know when to wash their hands because that is what they were taught on the course – but do they actually do it (properly)? They may know how to defrost a pie (but is this relevant to their work?). Another point to consider about certification is that a QCA accredited examination leads to a nationally recognised qualification. The QCA qualification and examination specifications require examination bodies to submit details of courses under headings such as:

- title of qualification;
- introduction;
- qualification aims;
- qualification structure;
- learning outcomes;
- national occupational standards;
- key skills;
- registration of training/examination centres;
- entry requirements and prior learning;
- preparation for the examination;
- form of assessment;
- examination results and awards; and
- progression opportunities.

The QCA insists that all training materials, learning outcomes, aims, objectives, examination papers, etc. have to be written in English. However, so long as an English version is provided at the time of the training, then materials may be made available in other languages for candidates.

However, in terms of improving food hygiene practice, checks should be made first to establish if attainment of the qualification was competency based, such as National Vocational Qualifications (NVQs), or if it was purely obtained through passing a multiple choice tick test or the completion of an end-of-course assessment such as an Intermediate Certificate in Hazard Analysis course. The Learning and Skills Council is responsible for awarding European Social Funding to training providers who meet specific criteria regarding learning and employment priorities in geographical areas in England and Wales. However, in some areas, funding seems conditional upon the number of beneficiaries who receive qualifications rather than any tangible evidence to show that competency based programmes have actually made positive contributions to, for example, food safety or a measurable reduction in notified cases of food poisoning.

The Food Standards Agency, QCA and Learning and Skills Council all need to speak to each other to find common ground regarding measuring improvements in food safety standards through competency based programmes whilst giving trainees the opportunity to gain a qualification or certificate. Until that happens the current nationally recognised accredited food hygiene certificates are outlined below:

The National Qualifications Framework has three levels which are relevant to food hygiene certificates. These are:

Foundation	A foundation for employees or potential employees. Equivalent to GCSE grades D to G. May be beneficial for positions such as catering assistants, bar staff, kitchen operatives, foundation in modern apprenticeship trainees or managers, where no formal training has been received.
Intermediate	These qualifications are aimed at food handlers working in craft or semi-skilled jobs. Equivalent to GCSE grades A to C. Examples of posts which may benefit include bartenders, commis chefs, advanced modern apprenticeship trainees, managers and supervisors (all of whom have received Foundation training).
Advanced	Advanced craft and management skills for managers and supervisors who have attended Intermediate courses or who have prior experience and suitable qualifications.

Further details may be obtained from the Qualifications and Curriculum Authority.
Visit www.qca.org.uk

The above levels in terms of food hygiene certificate courses may be summarised as follows:

♦ *Foundation (duration 6-9 hours)*

Foundation Certificate in Food Hygiene
Foundation Refresher in Food Hygiene Update

♦ *Intermediate (duration 18-24 hours)*

Intermediate Certificate in Food Hygiene (now Intermediate Certificate in Food Safety)
Intermediate Certificate in Hazard Analysis

♦ *Advanced (duration 36-42 hours)*

Advanced Certificate in Food Hygiene (now Advanced Certificate in Food Safety)

Further details of food hygiene qualifications available in the UK are listed in the chapter called "Choice of Courses and Trainers". The reader should contact the QCA or examination bodies for full details regarding the syllabus, assessment, and entry criteria.

Competency assessment must follow the training

For the training to have any use at all competency assessment of the food handlers who have undertaken training must take place. Up-to-date and accurate training records will have to be maintained. In addition, on returning to work it is a good idea for the trainees to have a meeting with their line managers to discuss how they are to turn the theory into practice. Too many managers, consultants who carry out audits, and enforcement officers who carry out statutory inspections, still place greater emphasis on ensuring that food handlers have a certificate or a training record. It would be better to observe and question a food handler's activities and test their implementation of food hygiene knowledge in the workplace. Some businesses use competency assessment cards. An example of a card on the market is shown on page sixteen.

A missed opportunity?

Some colleges and internal trainers do have their own competency-based food hygiene training programmes. These either support in-house training strategies or NVQs. The CIEH has a competence-based training and assessment programme available. Unfortunately it is, at present, only available to be used for trainees with learning difficulties or special needs. The UK food and hospitality industry needs more competency-based training programmes for all its employees. This will help to promote a sense of meaning and purpose, rather than just holding a certificate which has no expiry date on it.

What does the law say about certification or competency?

In short: not a lot. There have been a number of missed opportunities over the last 10 years. Current legislation tends to place the burden of proof more on the shoulders of proprietors of food businesses rather than requiring the enforcement officers to prove an offence. But, are enforcement officers themselves competent to make decisions about competency or certification when it comes to training, instruction and supervision or is it going to be left to business owners to decide how they meet the requirements of the law?

◆ The Food Safety Act 1990 (Section 23) permits local authorities to provide training for people who plan to set up a food business or for those already involved in a food business (such as proprietors, employees or otherwise). Other local authorities may contribute to another authority's expenses incurred in the running of a course. No definitions of training, certification or competency are given.

♦ The Food Premises (Registration) Regulations 1991 refers to the registration of food businesses operating in a local authority area. There is a prescribed form to be completed by proprietors of the businesses. It does ask for numbers of employees within the business, but not how or where training and/or instruction and supervision will take place.

♦ The Food Standards Act 1999 gives the Food Standards Agency authority to carry out educational or training activities. No definitions of training, competency or certification are given.

♦ The Food Safety (General Food Hygiene) Regulations, Schedule One, Chapter X 1995 require that "the proprietor of a food business shall ensure that food handlers engaged in the food business are supervised and instructed and/or trained in food hygiene matters commensurate with their work activity." There are definitions for food handler, food, food business and hygiene. No legal definitions of training, instruction and supervision are given. Nor is there any regulation that specifically states that a certificate is required by a food handler. These areas are considered further in the chapters about "Education and Training","Who Needs Training? and "The Role of Managers and Supervisors." In addition, an opportunity has been missed to spell out about how implementation is to be monitored and enforced.

♦ The Code of Practice issued under Section 40 of the Food Safety Act 1990 gives some advice about how the legislation is to be interpreted. Officers must pay due regard to relevant Industry Guides to Good Hygiene Practice. But there are still no definitions regarding training, instruction, supervision, competence, or certification. EHOs should not imply or state that attendance of any particular course is an express requirement. Nor should they imply that food handlers have to attend courses run by the local authority. Unfortunately, at the time of writing, this still happens.

♦ The Code of Practice gives no details about training or qualifications required by authorised officers to enable them to effectively train, instruct, supervise, assess competency or qualification. Enforcing authorities should arrange a minimum of ten hours' continuing development to enable them to effectively and legally enforce the provisions of the Food Safety Act 1990. Many of the universities offering degree courses in Environmental Health do not have specific modules to help undergraduates with these training issues. Maybe there should be a statutory post-graduate qualification in training and development for officers to enable them to be authorised to invoke Chapter X and subsequent training requirements.

♦ Industry Guides to Good Hygiene Practice: The reader should refer to the chapter in this book entitled "Who Needs Training?" for further discussion.

♦ The Children Act 1989: requires paid and volunteer adults who are responsible for looking after under-fives and children of statutory school age to receive adequate and suitable training to enable them to do their jobs and to ensure that the children in their care come to no harm. This includes food hygiene training, but the guidance give no indication of competency for the adults who are, because of the nature of their work, food handlers.

Visit www.doh.gov.uk/busguide/childhtm/annd.htm#hygiene for further information.

Is there a need to improve food hygiene training?

The following paper has been reproduced by kind permission of Richard A. Sprenger of Highfield.co.uk Ltd. The original may be found at www.highfield.co.uk

Most people would argue that training is necessary to enable staff to fulfil their potential, to effectively carry out their duties and responsibilities and to improve their skills. Effective training increases job satisfaction, improves performance and reduces the amount of instruction and supervision required.

It would therefore be reasonable to assume that the food safety training of food handlers should result in higher standards, improved food safety and a reduction in foodborne illness.

In the last ten years, millions of food handlers employed in the UK have successfully completed Foundation training courses provided by the Chartered Institute of Environmental Health, the Royal Institute of Public Health, the Royal Society for the Promotion of Health, the Society of Food Hygiene Technology (SOFHT) and, in Scotland, the Royal Environmental Health Institute of Scotland. In addition, many larger companies provide in-house training, which is of a comparable standard. Over the same period of time reported cases of food poisoning continued to rise.

Food poisoning usually results from the ignorance or negligence of food handlers somewhere in the food chain. However, it could be argued that the main cause of food poisoning is management failure, whether this is a failure to obtain the right type of equipment, the failure to design the premises correctly, a failure to have suitable contingency plans in place for the inevitable late delivery or equipment breakdown or the failure to provide effective instruction, supervision and training of food handlers. If this is the case, it would make more sense to ensure a greater priority was given to the training of supervisors and managers than first-tier workers. Companies with limited training budgets available would be better advised to ensure the satisfactory training of management, who would then be able to effectively supervise and train the food handlers for whom they were responsible.

Although nationally accredited food hygiene courses are an essential part of comprehensive food hygiene training, they should not be considered as being superior to competency-based training of food handlers on site. A pass mark of 66% in an examination, that can probably be successfully completed by the majority of food handlers without the benefit of attending a six-hour training session, should not be considered to be anything more than an indication that they may be competent with regard to food safety. It is possible to have a complete lack of understanding of cross-contamination and temperature control, to fail examination questions on these topics, and still achieve in excess of 66%. Furthermore, how relevant is an examination completed five or ten years ago if no additional training has been provided?

The Industry Guide to Good Hygiene Practice (Catering Guide) advises proprietors that:

"If agency staff cannot provide documentation then the proprietor should assume that they are not trained and deploy or supervise them accordingly."

Once again, this places too much significance on staff having certificates instead of deploying staff based on their knowledge and competence, which may be gleaned from questioning and observation.

Should we include terminology such as *Staphylococcus aureus, Clostridium perfringens,* binary fission and should we be differentiating between exotoxins, endotoxins and enterotoxins? Is it necessary to argue about whether we control hazards or risks? Are we training microbiologists or scientists, demonstrating the academic ability of the trainer or should we be concentrating on providing sufficient essential knowledge to enable food handlers to produce safe food? How many of us during training sessions apologise for discussing complex or non-relevant items, purely because "there might be an examination question on them".

Despite our knowledge of the main contributory factors resulting in food poisoning, there is no universal agreement or practical, consistent, scientific-based Government guidance on such important practices as:

♦ where to thaw frozen poultry;

♦ how to cool food in a warm kitchen;

♦ which parts of a food room should be disinfected; and

♦ the core temperature required for cooking/reheating meat (two minutes at 70°C is not particularly helpful).

If we are to ensure effective food safety training, I would suggest consideration of the following recommendations:

♦ we must provide incentives and encouragement to ensure the commitment of owners and managers to the benefits of food safety training and the effective supervision and guidance of trained staff. (The attitude of supervisors and the hygiene culture of an organisation must be positive to give the correct message to staff returning from food safety courses.) Too many food handlers are advised to ignore certain hygiene practices as being too expensive or time consuming;

♦ food businesses should implement food safety training programmes, which include standards for induction, awareness, formal, management and refresher training. The knowledge and skills required for each post should be documented. Regular knowledge and competency testing of all staff should be undertaken to ensure satisfactory performance and determine the need for refresher training;

♦ all accrediting bodies should carefully review their current courses and examinations to ensure the relevance of content and the appropriateness of their course regulations;

♦ stricter control must be exercised over the quality of registered trainers. A combination of adequate technical knowledge and good training skills is essential;

♦ all unnecessary jargon and scientific language should be removed from Foundation courses and examinations;

♦ courses should, as far as practicable, be less generic and the content should be of specific relevance to those attending;

♦ training and courses should be subsidised by the Government to encourage:

(a) training for short periods over several days or weeks. A six or nine-hour course held over one day does not produce the best results;

(b) smaller class sizes so that training can be more specific;

(c) competency based training at the work place;

♦ the examination pass rate should be increased to a minimum of 75% and incorrect answers to essential questions should result in candidates failing the examination;

♦ greater priority should be placed on effective training of managers and supervisors. It should be a legal requirement for high-risk food businesses to have at least one person on site who has the relevant qualification and experience;

♦ stricter control is required over the issue and use of certificates;

♦ increased emphasis should be placed on the importance of in-house competency based training and supervision;

♦ during inspections, authorised officers should assess the competence of food handlers by observations and questions, not by the presence of certificates on walls; and

♦ governments should provide consistent scientifically based guidance on good hygiene practice. (Preferably based on European Commission (EU) advice.)

Conclusion

Effective food hygiene training of managers, supervisors and food handlers is essential to reduce the risk of food poisoning. The UK has an enviable record with regard to food hygiene training, but continual improvement is necessary to maintain our position as one of the leaders. The link between existing statistics of reported incidents of diarrhoea and vomiting and the effectiveness of food safety training should be broken. Meaningful performance indicators must be identified, which accurately measure the effectiveness of food safety training and enable an assessment of changes to be made.

And finally, something to think about...

A cook-chill production unit in East London supplied 27 satellite units, two education authorities, a major airline, and a well known high street supermarket. In all there were some 250 food handlers. A food hygiene team of three was responsible for all aspects of food safety and food hygiene training. Application in the 1980s was made to one of the major food hygiene examination accredited awarding bodies. The team wanted to use their own examination paper because it reflected the work of the food handlers. The examination body would have none of it saying that the syllabus to be used did not follow a national syllabus. Here was a classic case of competency taking a back seat in favour of the need to generate money by the examination body. To demonstrate competency a stage further members of the food safety team were not allowed to carry out any food safety work until a month after taking up their posts. They had to work in all units and at all levels as food handlers. After that, every three months, one week was spent working in the cook-chill centre and a regeneration kitchen as a food handler. It undoubtedly made the team more competent in their work, and gave them experience of hands-on activities which they could pass on to the food handlers. They had a real understanding of the difficulties in being a food handler and could pass on important hygiene matters to their audiences without having to worry about whether a nationally recognised certificate was actually going to make any difference to competency.

The moral of this tale is that owners of food businesses and their staff may consider that there are some enforcement officers who are not competent to assess food handling practices because they have had no real hands-on experience in a food business. The officers cannot really appreciate how a business is run and how a kitchen brigade really operate. So do EHOs need more training about the real differences in the meanings and values of certification?

Further reading

- Food Safety Act 1990 Code of Practice. London: HMSO;
- Food Safety Act 1990 Practical Guidance. London: HMSO;
- Food Safety Act 1990. London: HMSO;
- Food Safety (General Food Hygiene) Regulations 1995. London: HMSO;
- Food Standards Act 1999. London: HMSO;
- Industry Guide to Good Hygiene Practice: Catering Guide (1997). London: Chadwick House Group Ltd; and
- Industry Guide to Good Hygiene Practice: Retail Guide (1997). London: Chadwick House Group Ltd.

2 Who Needs Training?

"Give a man a fish and you feed him for a day. Teach him to fish and you feed him for life." (Anon)

IMAGINE A COOK-CHILL PRODUCTION CENTRE

It has a high turnover of staff and relies on agency food handlers. The agency "trains" its food handlers to a Foundation Certificate in Food Hygiene. The cook-chill staff give the agency staff further training before they are let loose in the production kitchen. This was identified as a weakness in a HACCP system. Work experience students are given the menial task of emptying a large conveyor type dishwasher. The students are not told about the need to wear gloves. They stand near the curtain where the baskets of plates and pans exit from the dishwasher. Observers will see the students spitting on their fingers before retrieving the washed equipment. When asked why, the students say that the dishes are too hot to handle. What may have gone wrong here? How about, for example:

♦ HACCP systems failed to include training of all employees and part time employees (including work experience) in the use of the dishwasher;
♦ food handlers were not informed to let the equipment run the full length of the basket run after the discharge of the baskets with equipment from the dishwasher;
♦ food handlers were not shown how to avoid contaminating the plates; and
♦ managers failed to understand their responsibilities to supervise the food handlers in the correct use of the dishwasher and principles of cleaning & disinfection.

So who does need training?

Consider the definition for a "food handler", and then take a look at Appendix IV about HACCP and Training. So who in your opinion does need training?

Suggestions include, for example:

Proprietors	Chefs	Waiting staff	Agency staff	Child-minders
Managers	Commis chef	Bar staff	Part-time staff	Shelf-fillers
Supervisors	Sous chef	Baristas	Work experience	Teachers
Team leaders	Cooks	Cleaners	Care staff	Volunteers
	Catering assistants	Kitchen maintenance	Dieticians	Charity employees

The extent to which they need training will depend on training needs, career development, the types of hazards identified and the risks posed. It is important to remember training is not just about behavioural change at work. Training someone in the fundamentals of good hygiene practice at home may well reap benefits at work. Why? Because if behaviour can be changed in domestic catering practices, then employees may have more respect for what they are doing at work.

Was the correct training given?

This section illustrates examples of real events where training may have been given, but supervision was lacking. It is not known in every case if employees attended a Foundation Certificate in Food Hygiene course.

♦ Wedding reception part-time waitress was seen picking her nose as she carried vegetable dishes to reception guests.

♦ There is nothing like a scare to affect behavioural change. In 1996, over 400 guests were put at risk when a rice starter was put out four hours in advance at room temperature. 130 fell ill. The contract caterer revised their hazard analysis and identified the need for training at all levels of employees. After having their fingers burnt, the company has now developed a reputation as a centre of excellence.

♦ Think about the shop assistant who licks fingers to open bags, and then blows in the bags to give them some shape.

♦ A food handler in a major supermarket coffee shop used disposable gloves for everything. They were never changed and there was no visible sign of handwashing. On one occasion one glove had lost three fingers and the food handler carried on using the gloves. Just by chance the following day a customer complained to the environmental health department that three plastic glove fingers had been baked in her loaf of bread.

♦ There was the case of the sandwich bar food handler who spat on his fingers before taking hot rolls out of an oven.

♦ In another sandwich bar a girl cut her finger whilst preparing baguettes. She licked her wound and proceeded with her work. On the counter beside her there were three plastic chopping boards all embossed with "raw meats only" on the side. On the boards were piled alternating plates of sliced turkey and salmon. The food was uncovered.

♦ The owner/chef of a small restaurant insisted using the same yellow gloves to clean the customer toilet as he used in the pot wash.

♦ A manager sent all his employees on a foundation course, but would not let them change their practices upon return to work – because they would have held up speed of service.

◆ A schools' central production unit came under scrutiny when parents complained to a council environmental health department. The complaint regarded cold food at the points of consumption. EHOs checked the food in the various schools supplied by the unit. The average food temperature was 40 degrees Celsius. Back at the unit, catering assistance were observed taking and record temperatures of hot food. The temperatures were written down in a book. On closer inspection of the process it was observed that the probe was actually placed in contact with the bottom of the dishes in which the food was cooked, rather than the core of the food. The higher temperatures were then recorded in the book and no-one bothered to check the recorded temperatures.

◆ An oriental restaurant manager sent staff on a food hygiene course – not in their native tongue, but in English. The practice of defrosting duck, chicken and prawns altogether in the equipment sink was the same before and after the course.

◆ Before training, a care assistant thought it was more important to clean the floor than the raw chicken which she had dropped on it.

Some businesses with food hygiene managers and technicians insist that they work on the "shop floor" for at least one week every two to three months just to keep in touch with hygiene difficulties encountered by staff who handle food.

The training boom

The demand for food hygiene training within the UK started to grow in the early eighties. At the time it was seen as a means of preventing food poisoning. Little consideration was given to the role that basic food hygiene training had to play in the training and development of food handlers in the hospitality and food production industries. If six million people have undergone Foundation Certificate in Food Hygiene courses at approximately £30 per person that is nearly £2 billion worth of course fees. Has it been worth it?

At a unit level the answer must be *yes* – only if it results in:

◆ fewer customer complaints;
◆ an improved relationship with the local authority EHOs;
◆ reduced staff turnover;
◆ improved morale and motivation; and
◆ less food wastage.

For the individual food handler it has provided an opportunity for:

◆ a nationally recognised qualification;
◆ participation in the running of the business;
◆ involvement in the food safety culture; and
◆ improved standards at work and at home.

Nationally there does not appear to be a satisfactory answer. The reader should now be in a position to draw their own conclusions!

Education of food handlers has a major role to play by identifying the possibilities that appropriate education and training both have to keep good standards of food safety.

Hotel and catering businesses have seen benefits in training and are aware of the range of training organisations which provide a range of nationally recognised courses. More recently insurance companies are insisting on training food handlers in food hygiene. From the training and development perspective, the benefits include:

- ◆ staff motivation;
- ◆ setting standards, staff retention;
- ◆ a better trained workforce;
- ◆ receipt of nationally recognised certificates;
- ◆ the opportunity to fulfil some of the criteria which need to be met for the National
  - · Training Awards (NTAs), Investors in People (IiP), and National Vocational Qualifications (NVQs); and
- ◆ core skills as part of the Hospitality Foundation in Modern Apprenticeship programme.

An outline of the hospitality industry in the UK

In 1995-96, one in ten of the UK workforce was employed in the hotel and catering industry. The range of posts included food handling, administration, maintenance and marketing. There were approximately 100,000 restaurants and 77,000 pubs, not to mention hotels, catering contract units and clubs. In excess of three million people now work as paid food handlers. In 2001 the hospitality industry in the UK employed approximately 1.35 million people. One in three employees in the industry are catering assistants or kitchen porters. According to the Hospitality Training Foundation, during 2001, an estimated 17% of the workforce held no qualifications at all. The majority are in the hospitality industry. Care workers, nursing staff, child-minders, teachers, retail staff and leisure industry employees should not be forgotten. Various economic forecasts indicate that, for example, in London, there will be an extra 20,000 new hospitality posts before 2010. The biggest increase in positions will be for part-time staff (who may be holding down one or more jobs).

Employment turnover in the hotel and catering industry is high, especially for hourly paid staff. In a survey carried out by John Roberts in 1993 it was established that turnover was extremely likely in:

- ◆ the first six weeks of employment;
- ◆ larger more centralised hospitality organisations;
- ◆ larger urban areas;
- ◆ fast food operations, especially in urban areas; and
- ◆ certain groups or cohorts of employees, including trainee managers, chefs, kitchen porters, and bar staff.

Training and development managers have to take these factors into account when planning basic food hygiene or any other level of training for their organisation. For independently run businesses who do not have training managers, provision of basic food hygiene and other courses may place a burden on overheads. The current national shortage of skilled chefs is causing major problems too.

Food hygiene training is an example of the application of the cognitive approach to education, in which it is expected that the provision of relevant information or knowledge will lead to a change in practice (Rennie, 1995). Coutts and Harding (1985) believed that effective training increases knowledge, changes attitudes and develops better employee practice.

The Foundation Certificate in Food Hygiene courses involve the use of systematic and planned training approaches. Systematic training is training which is specifically designed to meet defined training needs. It is planned and provided by people who know how to train, and the impact of training is carefully evaluated (Armstrong, 1994). Kenney and Reid (1988) define planned training as a deliberate intervention aimed at achieving the learning necessary for improved job performance.

It is worth remembering that training, when effective, can equip individuals with appropriate job related knowledge, skills and attitudes. The Foundation Certificate (and higher levels) in Food Hygiene has a place in the training and development of food handlers, but there is more to it than just sending staff on a six to nine hour nationally recognised course.

Benefits of food hygiene training

Sir John Harvey Jones in his BBC documentary "Trouble-shooter" (1990) stated that "we spend most of our adult lives at work. There is no way under-trained amateurs can beat the trained and practised professionals we are up against." With regard to food hygiene training perhaps some training is better than none at all in the fight to reduce food poisoning incidents. Hotelkeepers and caterers (especially those running small independent businesses) often regard training as a chore and a distraction from the key task of running a profitable operation. But used effectively training can benefit the individual as well as the business.

Organisational psychologists, such as Maslow, Argyris and McGregor, start with the view that there is, or can be, a genuine conflict between a human being and his or her work, between the satisfaction of the individual, and the needs of the organisation. Hence what is good for the individual is by no means always good for the organisation and vice versa (Evans, 1994). There are others such as Likert, Herzberg, Wigdor and House who have views about the interaction between employees and managers. The theory may for various reasons conflict with the reality of a particular situation.

The most frequently wanted training by employees and their employers in the hotel and catering industry are skills in food hygiene, management, information technology, health and safety, advanced craft and supervision. Where organisations have dedicated training managers or trainers they will need to consider the training needs of the organisation and the individuals, outstanding training from previous year, and training committee recommendations. The training needs will then need to be prioritised using criteria based on the organisation's needs and a plan developed. Such criteria may include criticality, legislation, cost, quality, and training availability. With regard to food handlers and their employers, there are considerable benefits to be gained from the provision of food hygiene training.

For the individual, provision of such a course as the Foundation Certificate in Food Hygiene may:

♦ increase job satisfaction;
♦ improve motivation;
♦ reduce sickness;
♦ encourage team work;
♦ provide a recognised qualification; and
♦ assist with achieving particular NVQs.

In a survey of 1319 employees by the Hotel & Catering Training Company (HCTC) in 1995, training was perceived by the employees as being necessary for the following reasons:

- to do the job better 57%
- to get promoted 18%
- to get qualifications 12%
- to receive a pay rise 8%
- to get a better job 5%

With regard to the business or organisation employing food handlers there are benefits in providing food hygiene training too. These include:

- a trained workforce;
- defence of due diligence under Section 21 of the Food Safety Act 1990;
- compliance with the statutory provisions of the Food Safety Act 1990;
- less food waste;
- reduced customer complaints;
- reduced food poisoning risk;
- reduced insurance premia;
- lower staff turnover;
- increased staff morale;
- the chance to have an input to Investors in People and National Training Awards assisting staff with gaining NVQs; and
- BS5750 and ISO 9000 criteria.

The same HCTC survey asked 319 employers about their perceived benefits in providing training. The results were as follows:

- higher quality and increased profits 40%
- staff proud of work 34%
- customer satisfaction 32%
- more repeat business 15%
- lower staff turnover 6%

Medium to large sized food businesses have the resources to carry out training needs analysis (TNA). A TNA is the examination of the organisation's present and expected operations and the staffing necessary to carry them out, in order to identify the numbers and categories of staff who need to be trained or re-trained. It must also refer to the training needs of an individual to enable him/her to reach the required standard of performance in his/her current or future job. Food handlers, legally, have to be trained and/or instructed in food hygiene matters commensurate with their work activity. A TNA will highlight who would benefit most from a Foundation food hygiene course or some other form of food hygiene training. It may also prove beneficial in staff retention and the way food is handled within an organisation. One unforeseen benefit of a TNA is to help an organisation comply with regulation 4(3) of the Food Safety (General Food Hygiene) Regulations 1995. This requires the proprietor of a food business to identify any steps in the activities of the business which are critical to ensuring food safety and ensure that adequate safety procedures are identified, implemented, maintained and reviewed. The provision of food hygiene training will be beneficial to the proprietor and employees to ensure that this regulation is complied with.

In 1984 the World Health Organisation (WHO) acknowledged that education and training are the basis of effective and long lasting improvements in the levels of food safety. The benefits derived from training in terms of consumer safety and increased staff awareness with regard to better food handling practices speak for themselves.

Statutory interventions

The benefits of food hygiene training have been recognised for decades. Before 1990 it was left up to the discretion of proprietors of food business whether or not employees were to be sent on recognised courses. This section outlines the background to legal requirement for the training of food handlers in food hygiene matters.

The Food Safety Act 1990 came into force in the UK on 1 January 1991. The Act is the most important legal instrument relating to the sale of food for human consumption and as such is applicable to all food premises. It strengthened existing legislation and penalties. Also the Act is an enabling Act, which allows Ministers to issue new regulations for securing food safety in England, Wales and in Scotland. Section 23 of the Act states that:

"(1) A food authority may provide, whether within or outside their area, training courses in food hygiene for persons who are or intend to become involved in food businesses, whether as proprietors or employees or otherwise.

(2) A food authority may contribute towards the expenses incurred under this section by any other such authority, or towards the expenses incurred by any other person in providing, such courses as are mentioned in subsection (1) above."

To enable the Minister to introduce regulations concerning provision of food hygiene training, draft regulations and consultative documents were sent to a wide range of interested parties such as local authorities, food wholesalers and retailers, professional and trade organisations. Two draft regulations were produced. In that period the food industry and the hotel and catering industry made steps to train their staff to a minimum of a Foundation level of food hygiene. The demand for nationally recognised courses grew. Rumours spread without any justification that food handlers *had* to hold a basic level food hygiene certificate even though no UK regulation existed to that effect.

During this period of consultation the Audit Commission produced a paper entitled "Safer Food: Local Authorities and the Food Safety Act 1990" which discussed the implementation of the Food Safety Act 1990. The Commission has an important duty under Section 27 of the 1982 Local Government Act, to report on the impact of government statutory provisions on the achievement of economy, efficiency and effectiveness by local authorities. 5000 food premises of various types were visited by local authority EHOs. Foundation food hygiene training was seen to be beneficial by the Audit Commission. The Commission also recognised that serious health problems can arise through ignorance of the principles of the safe operation of processes. The survey carried out showed that there was a clear link between good hygiene training and lower health risk. 68% of take-away premises had a health risk and the least number of trained food handlers, compared with 8% of hospitals which had a health risk and a high number of staff trained.

The Council of the European Communities issued a Directive 93/43/EEC on 14 June 1993 concerning the Hygiene of Foodstuffs. Schedule X of the Directive states that "Food business operators shall ensure that food handlers are supervised and instructed and/or trained on food hygiene matters commensurate with their work activity." EU member states have an obligation to introduce the Directive into their various statute books. On 15 September 1995 the Food Safety (General Food Hygiene) Regulations 1995 came into force. Schedule 1 Chapter X of the Regulations states: "The proprietor of a food business shall ensure that food handlers engaged in the food business are supervised and instructed and/or trained in food hygiene matters commensurate with their work activity." Much to the confusion of the proprietors (and some enforcement officers) there was no further explanation. The myth that a basic food hygiene certificate was a mandatory requirement had begun.

A Catering Industry Guide to good hygiene practice advises to catering businesses on how to comply with the Food Safety (General Food Hygiene) Regulations 1995. It is an official guide to the Regulations which has been developed in accordance with Article Five of the European Commission (EC) Directive on the Hygiene of Foodstuffs (93/43/EEC). The guide has no legal force, but local authorities must give it due consideration when they enforce the Regulations. For the hotel and catering industry, the relevant guide is comprehensive enough to enable general managers or training managers to decide which level of training is suitable for their employees. Independently run businesses can also use the guide to their benefit.

Part 3 of the guide is entitled "Food hygiene supervision and instruction and/or training". The title is taken directly from the Food Safety (General Food Hygiene) Regulations 1995 - Schedule 1 Chapter X. The guide identifies three stages of supervising/instruction/training. Different food handlers need different levels of training. These levels are categorised as A, B, and C. Category A is defined as food handlers who only handle low risk or wrapped food, category B as food handlers who prepare open high risk foods, and category C as food handlers who also have a supervisory role. The guide states that other staff who are not food handlers may need some instruction or training as a matter of good practice. The training need will relate to the actual job of the individual. It will also relate to the type of food they handle. The guide suggests that special arrangements will have to be made for employees whose first language is not English, or for employees who have literacy/learning difficulties. The guide states that all staff should be instructed to ensure that they work hygienically and that a greater degree of supervision may be needed for new staff awaiting formal training, for staff handling high-risk foods and for less experienced staff. Even when staff have received formal training the level of supervision must depend upon the competence and skill of the individual food handler. The guide suggests three levels of training and gives considerable detail concerning training.

There are three levels of food hygiene training suggested in the Catering Industry Guide to compliance. These are:

♦ Stage 1 Essentials of food hygiene
    Coverage: Handwashing, cuts, bowel disorders, sneezing
    For: All food handlers
    Format: In-house informal written or verbal instruction.

♦   Stage 2 Hygiene awareness training
    Coverage: Causes of infection, cross-contamination, food storage, waste disposal
    For: Food handlers such as on-site support and front-of-house activities NOT directly
    involved in preparation and personal handling of high risk open foods, for example,
    waiters/waitresses, counter staff, cellar and bar staff.
    Format: More formal in-house instruction developing a knowledge of the basic
    principles of food hygiene.

♦   Stage 3 Formal training
    ♦   a) For: Food handlers such as those that prepare and handle high-risk open
        food, for example, chefs, cooks, kitchen assistants, bar staff who prepare food.
        Format: A formal food hygiene course of approximately six hours.
    ♦   b) For: Food handlers such as those that prepare and handle any type of food,
        for example, managers, head chef, owners and/or operators of home catering
        or mobile catering businesses.
        Format: A formal food hygiene course of approximately six hours. It would also
        be regarded as good practice if these food handlers took further advanced
        training courses which deal with food hygiene in more detail and cover
        management and systems, having durations of 12 to 24 hours to 24 to 40 hours
        at more advanced levels.

Stage of Training	Legal Requirement	Type of Training	Advice on Good Practice	Type of Training
ESSENTIALS	All	Informal		
AWARENESS	Category A	Informal	Category D	Informal
FORMAL TRAINING	Category B & C	Formal Training	Category E	Informal

This guidance is only an indication as to how a proprietor may comply with the regulations
but also it may be possible for a food business to show that compliance with the regulations
may be achieved in other ways.   A summary may be shown as follows:
Category Examples
    ♦   **A** foodhandlers, for example, catering assistants;
    ♦   **B** commis chef, cooks, catering supervisor;
    ♦   **C** unit manager, chef managers;
    ♦   **D** buyers, engineers; and
                    of food handlers, area managers.

The requirements, suggested levels of training needed and types of courses recommended are referred to in the Industry Guide to Good Hygiene Practice: Catering Guide to Compliance with the Food Safety (General Food Hygiene) Regulations 1995 (ISBN 0-11-321899-0). "Health Surveillance and management procedures for food handling personnel" (Technical Report Series 785, WHO, 1989) provides useful advice too.

Local Authorities which are responsible for enforcing the provisions of the Food Safety Act 1990 must comply with the requirements of the Code of Practice made under Section 40 of the Act. In particular:

"69. Any assessment of training levels should give due consideration to relevant UK or EU Industry Guides to Good Hygiene Practice.

In assessing the level of training or instruction which should be expected of food businesses dealing with low risk foods, the food authority should recognise that in many cases the provision of suitable written or oral advice to a food handler and active supervision may be sufficient to satisfy legal requirements.

In giving any advice or guidance on the training of food handlers, the food authority should not imply that any particular examination or course provided by any training organisation is a mandatory requirement."

The industry has a range of different routes for those who are seeking qualifications. The routes are designed for individuals to build up their skills in a variety of ways, and to some extent to help employers get what they want.

Training in the hospitality industry

For those who have recently left school the options include:
- attendance at a college or university as a full time student;
- joining a training programme such as a Foundation in Modern Apprenticeship (FMA) or Advanced Modern Apprenticeship (AMA);
- going straight into employment; and
- e-Learning (which includes computer based training and on-line learning).

For employees who have experience in the industry the options include:
- working towards NVQs/Standard Vocational Qualifications (SVQs) with employers;
- attendance at a college part-time;
- taking a full-time college or university programme;
- distance learning or self study; and
- computer based training and e-Learning.

Accepted qualifications in the industry are varied. Examples include:
- NVQs/SVQs Level 1 and 2 Catering and Hospitality;
- NVQs/SVQs Level 3 Catering & Hospitality Supervisory Management;
- NVQs/SVQs Level 4 Catering and Hospitality Management;
- Business & Technology Education Council (BTEC)/SCOTVEC National and Higher National;
- Hotel & Catering International Management Association (HCIMA) Professional Certificate and Diploma;
- HCIMA Post Graduate Diploma;
- First Degrees/MBAs;

- ◆ NEBSM Certificate in Supervisory Management; and
- ◆ Certificate and Diploma in Management Studies.

The majority of the above qualifications listed will include some form of food hygiene training. For example, to achieve NVQs/SVQs level 1 and 2 an underpinning knowledge of food hygiene is required. Using a recognised Foundation Certificate in Food Hygiene to support evidence for accreditation by prior learning and achievement is acceptable. The Foundation in Modern Apprenticeship and Advanced Modern Apprenticeships schemes enable young employees to gain job related skills, experience and qualifications. The schemes give employees the chance to move on to higher level NVQs and university degree courses. The FMA and AMA routes include NVQs and SVQs. Also they have a range of technical certificates. Depending upon the Modern Apprenticeship for Foundation or Intermediate level food hygiene certificates awarded by one of three accredited examination bodies are required.

The Department of Education and Skills has appointed the Hospitality Training Foundation (HtF) as the Service Skills Council to develop and maintain NVQs/SVQs for the Catering and Hospitality Industry and the Licensed Retailing Sector. The HtF advises the NCVQ and SCOTVEC. Advice is given by HtF to BTEC, City and Guilds, HCIMA etc. NCVQ and SCOTVEC accredit these organisations.

A major reason for the introduction of NVQs/SVQs was the need to improve existing skills and to try to do something about the fact that fewer young people are entering the labour market.

Organisations such as the Restaurant Association, British Hospitality Association (BHA) and HCIMA, etc. involved in training and development have access to a range of skills. The market is full of professional and technical advisers who are only too willing to give advice with regard to food hygiene training.

Investment in training and development has mainly been due to competition and legislation (i.e. the Food Safety [General Food Hygiene] Regulations 1995). However, take-up of NVQs/SVQs by the hotel and catering industry has been lower than in any other industry. Candidates are still opting for the other qualification routes listed above. For many employers and employees the NVQ/SVQ route is too time consuming and involves additional expenses. The recent recession and world terrorism threats have not helped independently run businesses. This in turn has dented any enthusiasm for training and development for staff.

The majority of training still occurs within the larger companies which make up the overall smallest proportion of the industry. Of over 180 catering and hotel companies surveyed by Roberts in 1994:

- ◆ 18% reported they were involved in or considering involvement in NVQs;
- ◆ 60% possessed a training plan; and
- ◆ 10% were involved in or considering Investors in People.

Whether NVQs, amongst other training initiatives, actually deliver a sizeable increase in effective training remains to be seen. Rarely are requests made in job advertisements for potential employees who are in possession of NVQs. Employers are increasingly asking for potential employees who have a Foundation Certificate in Food Hygiene.

Food handlers taking up employment for the first time, will be put through the Foundation Certificate in Food Hygiene course, if company policy dictates that all food handlers must have this qualification. Some companies make food handlers resit the examination if they are new to the company, while others are still not clear about the parity of courses organised by awarding bodies. Supervisors and managers who are promoted are being increasingly required to obtain an Intermediate or Advanced level food safety qualification. Before they can do this they usually have to obtain a Foundation Certificate in Food Hygiene.

Training and development in the past has been delivered in two ways:

  a)   attendance at formal external courses and training programmes
  b)   observation and participation in the workplace.

Over the last decade these more traditional approaches have been consistently extended. Currently catering and hotel businesses are operating a much wider range of training and development methods. Evidence for this can be seen with the introduction of NVQs and in the way Foundation food hygiene courses are being delivered. Companies or businesses should:

- identify the specific training needs of the company, business, and employees;
- design, resource, deliver, monitor and evaluate training and development activities; and
- review and report on training outcomes (larger companies).

At the beginning of this section the different routes to employment in the industry were outlined. An indication of the range of qualifications available was also given. For businesses with the resources to devote to training and development the opportunities are enormous. For individuals who have little support then problems will undoubtedly arise. Hyland, writing in the Daily Telegraph in 1996 was quoted as saying "There seems to be evidence to suggest that NVQ schemes launched ten years ago are a disaster. They have failed to develop skills to keep industry competitive and devalued training."

Until an alternative to NVQs is established, training and development of employees will continue to be best achieved in-house and by attendance at college where individuals have the chance to pick up "traditional qualifications". Furthermore, NVQs require considerable supporting machinery in the form of training assessors and verifiers, as well as the time and personnel with time in which to conduct the training.

The role and organisation of training

Food hygiene training may help to build teams both back and front of house. Training and development of food handlers will affect the operational functions, strategic planning and management issues. Staff are an expensive resource, and the success of any business in part relates to their individual ability to perform effectively. Training and development can assist by:

- ensuring they have the necessary skills and knowledge to undertake their duties, tasks and responsibilities;
- providing a set of standards to which employees can and should perform;
- encouraging their on-going development;
- providing increased motivation and job satisfaction;
- providing opportunities for self advancement;
- minimising personal risk; and
- training them in customer care.

By guiding food handlers in food hygiene matters such as personal hygiene and food handling, risks of food poisoning and possible legal action will be reduced. Food handlers will be aware of their legal responsibilities about not handling food when they have diarrhoea and/or vomiting, and they will be aware of the obligations under which their employers are placed to ensure that food is fit for consumption.

Customers will also benefit if training and development of employees is properly organised to ensure that:

- ◆ catering businesses which are effectively managed can provide services of value and quality, enhancing the customer's experience;
- ◆ the safety and quality of services and facilities are directly affected by the qualities and effectiveness of training;
- ◆ when problems occur, properly trained staff will be able to deal with these in an effective way;
- ◆ customers' needs and expectations will be correctly identified and services amended to meet the needs; and
- ◆ the risk to customers in respect of unsafe practices and procedures is reduced.

Most of all, food complaints and food poisoning will be reduced – but only if the knowledge is put into practice and the effectiveness of training is monitored.

Training qualifications for trainers

"Trainers are not born. They are bred "(Anon). To become a trainer takes time and patience. It can be very rewarding, but conversely it can contribute to innumerable difficulties if not thought out. Contact some of the organisations shown in the table on page 35.

To register with one of the examination bodies as an approved trainer to run Foundation food hygiene certificate courses, the following criteria will normally have to be matched:

- ◆ a minimum suitable level of certificated food hygiene knowledge, for example: Advanced level certificate in food hygiene, or higher such as BSc in Environmental Health, MSc in Food Safety and Control;

- ◆ a qualification in training or teaching, for example, Professional Trainers Certificate, Certificate in Health Education awarded by the Health Development Authority, BA in Education, Qualified Teacher Status, NVQ III or IV, City and Guilds 7303 or 7254 (for example); and

- ◆ experience in the food/catering industry or in teaching food studies in schools or colleges of further and higher education.

Every potential trainer should make further enquiries to the awarding bodies.

However, there is no legal requirement or need to register if in-house courses or training programmes are tailor made to suit the needs of particular employees and the business. However, a lack of training experience and knowledge about the subject may do more harm than good. Remember: proper planning and preparation prevent problems!

Name	Telephone	Website
Chartered Institute of Personnel and Development	020 8971 9000	www.cipd.org.uk
Institute of Training and Occupational Learning	0161 483 4577	www.itol.co.uk
The Chartered Institute of Environmental Health	020 7928 6006	www.cieh.org.uk
The Royal Institute of Public Health	020 7580 2731	www.riph.org.uk
The Royal Society for the Promotion of Health	020 7630 0121	www.rsph.org
The Royal Environmental Health Institute of Scotland	0131 225 5444	www.rehis.org
Colleges of Further and Higher Education	Consult Yellow Pages or your local telephone directory	

Surveys can be misleading

Occasionally surveys can be misleading. For instance, consider the following survey carried out for the Food Standards Agency (FSA):

Catering Workers Hygiene Survey 2002
Thursday, 31 October 2002

The largest-ever survey of food hygiene knowledge among catering industry workers was carried out between 15 April and 25 May 2002.

- more than 1,000 workers and managers in small independent catering businesses were interviewed;
- the survey revealed that more than a third of staff (39%) are neglecting to wash their hands after visits to the lavatory whilst at work;
- the research also demonstrated that half of all those interviewed (53%) did not appear to wash their hands before preparing food;
- just over half (55%) of the businesses in the survey had been in operation for under two years and two thirds (70%) employed up to four full time employees;
- less than two thirds (59%) of the catering workers questioned had a Foundation Certificate in Food Hygiene;
- only 3% of catering managers interviewed said retaining skilled, trained staff was important to their business; and
- only 32% believed good food hygiene practices were important to their business compared with 64% who saw good food as the key to keeping their customers.

The full details of the survey on page 35 are available on the FSA's website.

Handwashing: How many non-paid food handlers and families make a point of washing hands properly after going to the lavatory? They too can pick up bugs and contaminate food for family and friends. Does the population as a whole consistently wash its hands before handling food? Practical training in handwashing techniques is not included in the Foundation Certificate in Food Hygiene. Questions in the examinations merely ask candidates about when and not how hands should be washed. If managers do not know how to wash hands or teach it, and there are generations of parents who are poor at handwashing, how is the food handler expected to know what to do? So who needs training in handwashing? The answer: teachers, trainers parents, families, employees, supervisors and managers. Compare the Agency's figures with 26% of men and 17% of women who do not always wash their hands before handling food, or 31% of men and 17% of women who do not regularly wash their hands after visiting the toilet at *home* (source: Food and Drink Federation for food**link** survey in 2002).

Certificate in basic food hygiene: The Agency failed to make it clear in their press release that the basic certificate is now called a Foundation certificate, and also that there is no legal requirement to hold a certificate. Also, some candidates may have not sat the examination or failed the examination due to illness, language barriers, basic skills needs or special needs. It was once said that if "you handle food you have a licence to kill someone" even if you hold a certificate.

"Only 3% of catering managers interviewed said retaining skilled, trained staff was important to their business." Compare this figure to the Hospitality Training Foundation's report entitled "Training and Development Review 2002". It provided an in depth analysis of training and development within the hospitality industry. 800 employers and others across Great Britain were involved in interviews. 79% of respondents said that training operational staff improved customer relations, staff efficiency was improved (71%), as was staff productivity (54%). Food hygiene training was seen as important if the current legislation was to be complied with. Experience together with qualifications was seen as important for career development within the industry.

So who does need training?

In short, everyone who handles food! The general public, educators, enforcers, trainers, mentors, employees, supervisors, managers and proprietors all need increased awareness about food hygiene. To what extent will depend upon their individual circumstances. If they work in, or run a food business, individual career development, employee motivation and, of course, the findings of the hazard analysis or HACCP will determine the answer.

Further reading

- Armstrong, M (1987) *Human Resources Management: A case of the Emperor's new clothes?* London: Personnel Management;
- Coutts, LC and Harding, LK (1985) *Teaching for Health*. London: Churchill Livingstone;
- HtF (1995) *Training Who Needs it?* London: Hospitality Training Foundation;
- HtF (1999) *Look Who's Training Now*. London: Hospitality Training Foundation;
- HtF (2001) *Skills and Employment Foresight*. London: Hospitality Training Foundation;
- HtF (2002) *Labour Market Review*. London: Hospitality Training Foundation;

- Industry Guide to Good Hygiene Practice Catering Guide (1997). London: Chadwick House Group Ltd;
- Kenney, K and Reid, M (1988) *Training Interventions*. London: IPM;
- LSCLC (2002) *Local Strategic Plan 2002-05 Central London*. London: Learning and Skills Council;
- WHO European Service No.15 (1983) *Mass catering*. Geneva: World Health Organisation; and
- WHO Technical Report Series 785 (1989) Health surveillance and management procedures for food handling-personnel. Geneva: World Health Organisation.

3 The Role of Managers and Supervisors

"It is noble to be good, and it is nobler to teach others to be good – and less trouble!" (Mark Twain 1835-1910)

Management skills

If licensing ever hits food businesses, the law makers in the UK will need to think very clearly about the benefits of licensing managers rather than the food businesses. After all to sell alcohol a licence is required. To prepare a potentially lethal meal does not. Managers of food businesses frequently have little or no management skills training. Something like 98% of all food businesses in the UK employ fewer than ten employees.

What is management? Perhaps it could be defined as "the art of getting four food handlers to do the work of four food handlers." It is unfortunately based on more than a simple definition. Essential management skills required are:

♦ leadership;
♦ motivation;
♦ training/coaching;
♦ team building;
♦ communication;
♦ cultural awareness; and
♦ influencing.

With these skills, plus suitable and sufficient food hygiene training a manager of a food business will be able to identify food safety training needs. The manager will be able to:

♦ observe employee job performance;
♦ question or survey employees to identify areas of weakness;
♦ review past health inspection reports for violations related to employee performance; and
♦ test employees' food safety knowledge.

An IPM consultative document, "Managing People – The Changing Frontiers", published in Personnel Management during November 1993 stated that: "There is an increasing awareness that all managers will need a better understanding of how to manage and lead people…However…the implications in terms of training and development required are not yet fully appreciated." The quotation is equally relevant today, particularly in small and medium sized food businesses employing fewer than 250 and especially in small businesses that have fewer than ten employees.

Essential management skills

Let us look at one of the essential management skills listed above. "Influencing" – what does it mean? Below are six sections which will help the manager to influence people at work. The questions are deliberately provocative. They may raise further questions about a manager's level of training and ability to put into practice what has been taught.

1. Watching: If you want to learn how staff work just watch them. Consider how many times they wash their hands in a food room, or how they use disposable gloves. There is no need to talk to the staff. Behavioural patterns will be picked up and identified. How do the staff interact? Is the sous chef setting an example to the kitchen porter? Do the staff shut the back door after a delivery?

2. Listening: Does the Head Chef motivate or shout at staff? Do employees comment how senior managers never set an example when in a food room? Maybe if someone finds some hygiene or food safety problem such as incorrect temperatures or mould then they need to talk to someone. How is the message conveyed and acted upon?

3. Understanding: Employees have now been watched and listened to. Build up some kind of picture of the food handlers that matter. Are they managing to succeed or succeeding to fail in their post because, for instance, no one in the business has helped them to apply the knowledge gained on a course in a practical way? Perhaps the observer might like to reminisce about the practical application difficulties they ran into as a trainee or fresh out of catering college.

4. Be part of the picture: How does the staff see the observer? Never set an example? "Do as I say but not do as I do?"

5. Influencing: Establish how much influence you may have. How is it applied and received? Has the influencing succeeded or failed? Maybe there was a better or alternative way that the situation could have been handled?

6. Changing: Food hygiene practices will not be changed overnight. It is better to lead and motivate employees. Start off with something small and use that as a building block. For instance it could be handwashing, or changing the uniform, or encouraging hygiene discussions at brigade meetings, etc.

Another of these skills is "communication". Just how well qualified is a manager to assess the English capabilities of a food handler from overseas – especially when the manager may not have been born in the UK? This point is particularly relevant when considering sending food handlers on food hygiene courses that are run in a language that could be considered to be a "second language". Britain has perhaps the worst record in the EU of failing to have an adequate workforce who can speak two or more languages. Failure to communicate represents a major food safety issue.

As yet there is no legal requirement for managers of food businesses to show that they are competent or certificated in any of the essential management skills. If there were, then managers would become more involved in the practical implementation of food safety and hygiene matters by themselves and their employees.

A problem frequently encountered in the food and hospitality industries is the high turnover of employees – especially at the lower end of the scale. But even these days with a highly mobile workforce, managers and supervisors from a range of countries come and go. Whilst learning English and broadening their experience as managers they must not neglect their food hygiene management responsibilities. In 1984 a joint WHO/FAO Expert Committee on Food Safety identified that whilst food hygiene training was the most effective tool to train food handlers in hygiene practices, it was all too often neglected.

Some managers may be tempted to rely on medical screening and faecal testing as the way to reduce contamination by staff. These managers would be in a minority. Tests of this nature do not ensure good practice, and may be only as good as an MOT test for a car! Perfect headlamps in the garage, bulb blown on leaving the forecourt after the test; free from disease one day, ill the next.

Perhaps the worst employees to train within a food business are managers and supervisors. One of the main, reasons is that they feel that they have more to consider in the running of the business than just food safety. However, changing management attitudes and food hygiene practices are equally as important as changing attitudes and practices of other employees within the business. An effective manager will:

- set the required food safety standards;
- provide resources (such as equipment and training) to achieve standards;
- implement and devise systems to achieve standards (HACCP, for example);
- inform and discuss standards with employees;
- motivate and train employees;
- provide effective supervision; and
- monitor, review and improve performance.

Take a look at the next two sections and compare the diagrams. Consider what sort of management attitudes count. Decide if you are a good or bad manager. Advice about legal compliance and enforcement of the legislation is given. Throughout this chapter advice is given to managers and supervisors about how they can improve their own standards of training and develop a culture of food safety within the business.

For further in-depth reading about management of food hygiene, take a look at the reading list at the end of this chapter.

What sort of management attitudes count?

A good manager will think about and demonstrate some of the characteristics shown below:

Or, a bad manager will adopt unacceptable food safety practices:

The law and a defence of due diligence

Managers need to consider their "Defence of Due Diligence" under Section 21 of the Food Safety Act 1990. The section states "…it shall…be a defence for the person charged to prove that he took all reasonable precautions and exercised all due diligence to avoid the commission of the offence by himself or by a person under his control." Proprietors of food businesses have a legal obligation to sell food which is fit for human consumption, complies with food safety requirements, and is the substance, nature and quality as demanded by the consumer. Under Section 36 of the Food Safety Act 1990 directors and managers may be held directly responsible for contraventions if proved.

For the Defence of Due Diligence to succeed the manager must demonstrate how "all reasonable precautions" have been taken. In respect of training it is simply not enough to send employees on a classroom-based course without identifying the training needs of individuals and not giving them post-course practical supervision and guidance. Unless the employees are in jobs which require knowledge of multi-skilling, the traditional one day or longer food hygiene certificate courses may be totally inappropriate. The manager may also wish to consider written training records. Sound systems that can be demonstrated have two key advantages: a reduced risk of prosecution, and higher standards of food safety and hygiene which will increase consumer confidence.

Managers should be aware that enforcement officers have to consider their assessment of the level of supervision and instruction and/or training as follows:

- ♦ assessments have to be made with consideration to the EU or UK Industry Guides (such as the Industry Guide to Good Hygiene Practice for the Catering Industry);
- ♦ the relative level of risk in connection with the operation of the business;
- ♦ an equivalent training course, similar to an accredited food hygiene examination course, where the course content is similar – and relevant to the operation; and

◆ where low risk foods are concerned, written or oral information given to food handlers may satisfy the requirements of the legislation.

The local authority EHOs may give managers advice about how to meet the training requirements. The officers are not in a position to recommend any particular trainer. However, they can provide a list of trainers. The officers must not show favour towards any particular trainer or courses run by authorities.

The officers will adopt a graduated approach to enforcement action. Education and training is viewed as a legitimate part of enforcement. Officers will always discuss the supervision, training and/or instruction requirements and may be consulted by managers. If the business fails to respond to the informal educative approach, depending upon other significant breaches of food hygiene regulations, the EHO may serve an Improvement Notice on the proprietor to ensure that supervision, training and/or instruction take place.

Food premises will be inspected depending upon the inspection risk rating which they are given. There are four parts to the assessment.

Part 1 - Before determining the potential hazards in the premises, three factors will be considered:
◆ type of food and method of handling;
◆ method of processing; and
◆ consumers at risk.

Part 2 - In addition, current level of compliance with the legislation is considered. A scoring system is used to assess:
◆ food hygiene and safety (including temperature control and food handling practices); and
◆ structural and housekeeping matters.

Part 3 – Confidence in management and control systems is assessed. A premises in which management and the food handlers both understand the food safety management systems (and put them into practice) will receive a better score than one which has no implemented food safety system, or the staff are excluded from any safety management system. EHOs will consider the track record of the business, attitudes of management towards food safety and hygiene, knowledge about hazards, critical control points (HACCP) and other food safety matters.

Part 4 – Significance of risk will also be considered taking into account issues such as:
◆ potential for contamination and /or cross-contamination involving *Clostridium botulinum* and *E. coli* O157 (plus other VTEC);
◆ survival and growth of involving *Cl. botulinum* and *E. coli* O157 (plus other VTEC);
◆ evidence of food safety management systems which involve hazard analysis, proper implementation, and control measures which are recorded as part of a monitoring process; and
◆ suitable and relevant training of food handlers, *including* managers and supervisors. This includes evidence of theory taught on certificate courses.

Each of the previous issues is given a weighting which determines the minimum frequency of food hygiene inspections:

- ◆ Category A   at least every 6 months
- ◆ Category B   at least every 12 months
- ◆ Category C   at least every 18 months
- ◆ Category D   at least every 2 years
- ◆ Category E   Alternative enforcement strategy

The frequency of food standards inspections is as follows:

- ◆ · Category A   at least every 12 months
- ◆ Category B   at least every 24 months
- ◆ Category C   subject to an alternative enforcement strategy, but inspections must take place at least once every three years.

Both food hygiene and food standards inspections will take into account management attitude, staff training and technical knowledge.

The statutory Code of Practice dictates that high-risk premises are to be visited at least once every 12 months.

Proprietors and managers ought to be aware that under Section 23 of the Food Safety Act 1990, local authorities may provide training both inside and outside their area. In addition, officers carry out food hygiene inspections under the guidance of Code of Practice. The Code directs enforcement officers about how to conduct an inspection to ensure a business complies with the provisions of the Food Safety Act 1990. There is no statutory requirement to hold a Foundation or higher level food hygiene certificate. Officers should listen to and assess the means by which a manager can demonstrate supervision, training and/or instruction of food handlers to a level commensurate with their work activity.

If things go wrong between the local authority and the food business the manager may turn to the Local Authorities Co-ordinators of Regulatory Services (LACORS) registered in England as the Local Authorities Co-ordinating Body on Food and Trading Standards. It is responsible to the local authority associations in England, Wales, Scotland and Northern Ireland to assist the 467 local authorities in the United Kingdom to improve the quality of trading standards and food safety enforcement by promoting co-ordination, consistency and good regulation. Enforcement needs to be fair, even-handed, consistent and applied with common sense. Advice given to businesses and recommended remedial actions made are essential features of a modern enforcement system. Within that system legal proceedings and other enforcement sanctions are nevertheless necessary to protect consumers, prevent abuse or as a policy of last resort. Owners of food premises in more than one local authority area may find the "Home Authority" principle a useful vehicle for developing a common training strategy throughout all its branches. For further information contact the local environmental health department in the authority where the head office is located.

Are managers food handlers?

Are managers and supervisors food handlers? In the chapter "Who needs food hygiene training?" a legal definition of a food handler in the Food Safety (General Food Hygiene) Regulations 1995 is given. A food handler in this instance is defined as: any person in a food business who handles food, whether open or packaged (food includes drink and ice).

Compare this with the definition given in the Institute of Food Science and Technology's "Food Hygiene Training: A guide to its responsible management" (1992). The definition reads:

"**A food handler means any person involved in a food business who, by his actions, or management, or decision, or advice, can influence the hygiene or quality of any food handled by that business at any stage.**"

The Royal Institute of Public Health (RIPH) uses the same definition. "Any person" therefore could be extended to the General Manager, Purchasing Manager, Supervisors, Accountants, and others involved in the operation of a food business – not just chefs, kitchen porters and catering staff.

The WHO Working Group on Health Examinations of Food Handlers' unpublished report in 1980 defined a food handler as "… a person in the food trade or someone professionally associated with it such as an inspector who, in his routine work, comes into direct contact with the food itself…" during all stages from production to direct consumption.

The managers of food businesses need to demonstrate an awareness of current legal requirements for food hygiene, safety and standards (composition, quality and labelling). In addition s/he must demonstrate that they have taken appropriate steps to inform, train, keep up-to-date and supervise their employees. Make use of the local authority environmental health department for advice and training. It is better to ask early rather than to receive a visit at an inopportune moment!

A not uncommon situation

Consider this: a kitchen porter attends a one-day food hygiene certificate course for career development, and a waiter attends a one day course after being instructed to by the manager. Their line manager has received a similar level course. The candidates return from their courses with new ideas. However, there is no-one in their premises who can help them put their new found theoretical knowledge into practice. The manager does not lead by example and has forgotten what was learnt on her course five years beforehand. This results in demotivated staff and no visible improvement in food hygiene standards within the business.

What are better solutions?
♦ the manager needs to develop a training strategy and seek advice about effective training methods;
♦ if the subordinates are to attend courses perhaps they could have been shown how the courses provide underpinning knowledge for NVQs in Food Preparation, or Foundation in Modern Apprenticeships;
♦ the manager's HACCP or food safety management system may have identified the best form of training;
♦ was the one day course suitable for a multi-skilled employee or a job specific employee?
♦ did the manager enquire about the subject matter – for instance if s/he runs a vegetarian restaurant why (for example) are the candidates being examined on their knowledge of defrosting chickens?
♦ was any consideration taken into account of the employees' levels of English, special needs or any learning difficulties?

- the manager could consider higher level courses (such as Intermediate or Advanced Certificate in Food Safety) to enable effective practical management of food hygiene; and
- the manager should sit down with the candidates on their return from their respective courses and put together a "commitment to action plan". This will enable the manager and subordinates to work together to practically improve standards.

Failures of management

Dr Richard North, in researching common contributory factors associated with food poisoning outbreaks, has identified ten top failures of management. These are:

- failure to carry out risk assessment on change of ingredients, processes or recipes;
- lack of or inadequate contingency planning;
- management disincentives to maintaining hygiene standards;
- lack of communication between decision makers and risk-takers or observers;
- failure to recognise flawed (potentially hazardous) procedures;
- lack of or inadequate post-incident evaluation and implementation of findings;
- lack of stability in operations and/or management;
- absence of routine planning and/or defined and consistent procedures;
- commercially driven misuse of equipment or premises; and
- unrealistic demands on the operation, preventing adequate risk management.

The following ten "rules" for managers and supervisors are reproduced by kind permission of Dr Richard North (1999) from his thesis work entitled "A management perspective on the causation of food poisoning."

It should be emphasised that this model does not replace food handlers' rules. It is intended to provide a specific focus for those in management positions in food operations. However, the formulation of such rules, based on the identification of "management perspective" causal factors, in food poisoning incidents, offers exciting possibilities for improved prediction and control of food poisoning risks in commercial premises.

1.	Carry out risk assessments before making changes to any ingredients, processes or recipes, and implement any new safety requirements identified.
2.	Be prepared for breakdowns, crises or unexpected changes - plan alternative arrangements for the production, storage and/or delivery of high risk foods.
3.	Check whether your management systems or structures penalise staff for maintaining good hygiene - do your staff lose out if they stick to the rules?
4.	Make sure bad practice and hazards can be notified to people who have the authority to deal with these problems, and pass back information on hazards down the chain.
5.	Ensure that systems and processes are regularly reviewed by persons who are fully competent to recognise hazards and report on them.
6.	Rapidly and fully investigate any food safety incidents (food poisoning, etc.), evaluate the findings and ensure that any changes needed are fully implemented.

7.	Identify and eliminate conflicts between "best practice" and actual working practices, whether arising from unit design or management/commercial requirements.
8.	Establish safe procedures for all high-risk operations and check to see that they are carried out consistently.
9.	Prevent the misuse of equipment and do not allow (or require) production levels over and above the safe capacity of the operation.
10.	Make sure your staff (and your under-managers/supervisors) have the means, knowledge and resources to carry out your instructions on good practice.

The model above will only be effective if the managers have received proper training not only in food hygiene management but also in management of personnel. Managers and supervisors will need to have a special understanding of specific food safety risks inherent in their operation. This will be provided by effective training. (Changes in policy or practice could therefore lead to the cause of food poisoning or a failure in food safety). When EHOs investigate outbreaks they may well be asking the manager or supervisor about:

- practices;
- procedures;
- personnel;
- equipment;
- recipes;
- suppliers;
- customers; and
- training, etc.

If the manager is asked a question by the EHO about suppliers it is not enough to say "We have used them for years", or in answer to a question about recording temperatures to say "They are recorded twice a day". Fine – but what safety checks have been made on the supplier rather than taking their service for granted, and why bother taking temperature readings twice a day? Are the staff trained how to inspect food deliveries, and what to do if temperature readings are unsatisfactory? Positive answers to demonstrate a practical knowledge of the theory taught on courses or during one-to-one sessions are necessary.

Managers have a responsibility to ensure that the premises are hygienic. A premises may be clean, and yet be unhygienic. The report into the 1996 East Lanarkshire *E. coli* O157 outbreak, which affected 500 people, identified that the butcher's shop at the centre of the investigation was clean. However, the manager failed to maintain safe systems to ensure food safety. In 2002 a manager in Earl's Court (Central London) was fined £31,000 for offences under the Food Safety Act 1990. Part of his defence was that he had received Hazard Analysis training and attended an Intermediate level course – but had to admit that the theory was not passed on to his employees, nor did he put into practice what he had been taught. Other examples of prosecutions relevant to training and supervision include the following:

- June 2000, a hotel proprietor in Birmingham was fined £5,000 for extensive cockroach activity, and failure to monitor compliance with company hygiene policies. Training had taken place but there was no practical implementation;
- October 2000, a fish restaurant owner was fined £3,500 for unhygienic premises and poorly trained staff;
- August 2001, the owner of a restaurant in Nottingham was fined £5,900 for 32 offences under the Food Safety Act 1990 and Food Safety (General Food Hygiene) Regulations 1995. One of them related to "untrained food handlers left to run the business unsupervised"; and
- October 2001, a grocery shop owner in North London had an Emergency closure imposed upon it. The court were told about unhygienic conditions and staff who had no food hygiene knowledge.

Hygiene management therefore involves:

♦ a knowledge of basic microbiology to preserve food and prevent food poisoning;
♦ knowledge of hazard analysis implementation or some other appropriate system;
♦ prevention of product contamination and pest infestation; and
♦ organisation, co-ordination and direction of personnel, food premises and equipment.

MANAGEMENT RESPONSIBILITIES

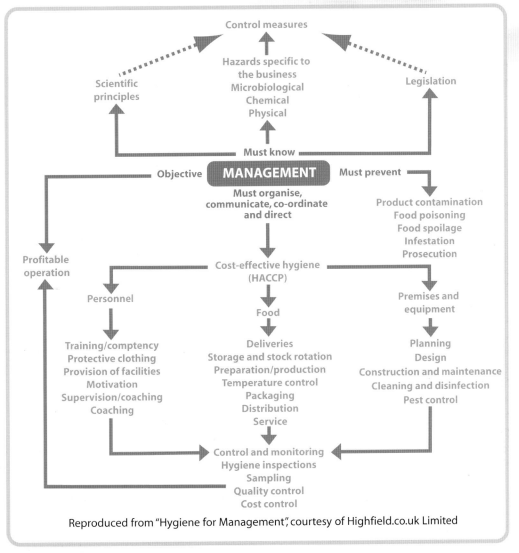

Reproduced from "Hygiene for Management", courtesy of Highfield.co.uk Limited

Lateral or creative thinking

It is important for managers to adopt the "What if?" line of thought. The alternative line of thinking, "It has never happened here, so it is of no consequence to my business", will only lead to disaster. Food safety management involves a degree of lateral or creative thinking. But all levels of employees have to be involved if an effective food safety culture (which demonstrates an understanding of good food hygiene standards) is to be established.

Food safety cultures

A culture could be defined as "the way we do things around here". The "we" refers to managers and junior employees alike. Everyone in the business should be encouraged to help in the development of a food safety culture. Adopting the Business Excellence Model approach suppliers and customers should also be involved.

There is little excuse for a manager to have less food safety training than a subordinate. Likewise if a new subordinate has had experience of food safety in a previous job then he or she should be encouraged to share that knowledge.

Team or brigade meetings are useful vehicles to discuss hygiene topics such as handwashing. However, the manager must ensure that they always practise what they preach. If the premises has a computer consider access to the internet. There is a considerable amount of information available about food safety training and advice.

The manager should encourage employees to learn from the advice available. Never overlook the advice given out by local authorities on their websites. It is common to find a considerable wealth of information which has relevant food hygiene training themes. The FSA's website is split into two parts for consumers and owners of businesses.

Managers must be aware that food handlers who require the most food hygiene training will be directly involved in the handling of high-risk foods. The nature of the work involved will help with the selection and suitability of training or instruction programmes.

Thinking tactics

Reuven Feuerstein is generally acknowledged as the founding father in the field of determining skills and strategies necessary to make a person a free and independent thinker. The trainer and manager can use Feuerstein's Top Ten Thinking Tactics to help with problem solving, whether in the classroom, kitchen, dry store, etc. They can be applied straightforwardly – in some instances the tactics may help with the implementation of effective HACCP and the development of a food safety management system. These are:

1. pinpointing the problem;
2. systematic search;
3. planning - rehearsing a way forward before attempting a solution;
4. check and change - constantly checking on the way something is done and accepting the need for change;
5. correct communication - making instructions and wishes clear;
6. comparison and contrasting - seeing fine points of difference between apparently similar material or events;
7. getting the point - through the initial fog of confusing information, by comparing and contrasting, trying to detect a common theme;
8. using several sources - being able to think about more than one piece of information at a time, combining the pieces to make sense of the whole task;
9. self awareness - becoming aware of an individual's learning style; and
10. setting your own targets - understanding what your purpose is - and having ideas about what you want to achieve.

Trainers, managers, and supervisors need to know about the concepts, skills and strategies involved in human problem solving. Food handlers will be motivated, develop self-esteem, and be better learners if they have a better understanding of what they are doing and why they are doing it.

Managers and supervisors must be aware about the barriers that employees may face if being sent on a course or about to undertake a training session. Literacy difficulties, slow learners, English as a second language, and other special needs are just some issues discussed in the chapter about Barriers to Learning.

Suggested management responsibilities

Managers and supervisors who work in food premises have a number of food hygiene responsibilities. The list below is intended to act as a summary for managers and supervisors when they have their instruction and/or training hats on. For further guidance about managerial responsibilities in a more general sense the reader is recommended to use the reading list at the end of the chapter.

- ◆ be aware of their own and their employees' legal requirements in respect of instruction, training and supervision to ensure that these are commensurate with their work activities;
- ◆ understand that the legal requirements provide for minimum food hygiene standards. Managers and supervisors should strive for higher levels;
- ◆ set a good example to subordinates. For instance, if instructing them about handwashing, managers must be seen to wash their hands on entering a food room and in the manner which is expected;
- ◆ involve employees in the food safety management decisions and discuss food safety issues at team meetings. Give employees the opportunity to make suggestions at the meetings, face to face, or to write them down in a food safety comments book. This method is often disregarded as a training method – but it can be put down to part of the learning experience;
- ◆ managers need to keep up-to-date. They need to attend refresher or higher levels of training. Going to hospitality and food safety exhibitions or conferences, or attending local food clubs and food safety forums will help to keep the manager's knowledge up-to-date;
- ◆ learn how to carry out food hygiene audits and observe individuals performing food handling tasks. Ask questions to assess the need for further training;
- ◆ help individuals who do not speak English as a first language if they are being sent on food hygiene courses which are only to be delivered in English. Many colleges run food preparation courses combined with English skills. Do not assume that a non-English speaking food handler will be able to cope on a course;
- ◆ use the hazard analysis critical control point system as a management tool. This will help to highlight training, instruction and supervision needs;
- ◆ include food handling and hygiene in all training courses related to food and catering training; and
- ◆ attend higher levels of food hygiene courses if dealing with highly vulnerable groups of people, in addition to running high-risk food premises.

Where next?

Mike Jacob in his *Safe food handling: a training guide for managers of food service establishments* (Geneva, WHO, 1989) recommends that managers should organise the training of their food handlers and themselves take responsibility to supervise operational procedures.

To sum up, effective food safety management will require managers to start reviewing the following:

♦ implementation of existing, or production of an effective, HACCP;
♦ the impact of current food safety legislation on their business and employees;
♦ identification of suitable quality assurance systems, such as ISO 9002:2002;
♦ designing a quality assurance system to suit the needs of the business;
♦ developing a safety culture;
♦ seeking advice from enforcement and education agencies, in addition to funding providers;
♦ setting an example; and
♦ providing the tools for individuals to do their job.

To ensure effective food hygiene training, managers will need to:

♦ be adequately trained themselves;
♦ know how to supervise staff in food hygiene matters;
♦ be responsive to suggestions and comments which may contribute to improved standards;
♦ review systems and change practices/processes as necessary; and
♦ help staff in putting food hygiene theory into meaningful practice.

In 1992, Maureen Wisdom (a Surrey based food hygiene adviser) published an independent survey about the effectiveness of basic food hygiene training. Her key recommendation was for managers and supervisors to receive training first. The training should be to levels 2 or 3 (namely Intermediate or Advanced certificates in food hygiene). This, according to Wisdom, would help them appreciate the importance of monitoring their staff as well as training them. Sound observations indeed! But, management skills and training skills are also required if managers and supervisors are going to make any impact upon food hygiene in their business.

Further reading

♦ CBI (1990) *Developing a Safety Culture*. London: Confederation of British Industry;
♦ Department of Health (1986) *The Report of the Committee of Inquiry into an Outbreak of Food Poisoning at Stanley Royd Hospital*. London: HMSO;
♦ East, J (1993) *Managing Quality in the Catering Industry*. London: Croner Publications Ltd;
♦ Evans, D (1994) *Supervisory Management: Practices and Principle*. London: Cassell;
♦ Hayter, R (1994) *Safety in Catering: A Guide for Managers and Supervisors*. London: MacMillan;
♦ IFST (1992) *Food Hygiene Training: A Guide to its responsible management*. ISBN 0905367103 London: IFST;
♦ Jacob, M (1989) *Safe food handling: a training guide for managers of food service establishments*. Geneva: World Health Organisation;

- Johns, N (1995) *Managing Food Hygiene*, London:Macmillan Press;
- North, R (1999) *Some Observations on Food Hygiene Inspections*. London: Chadwick House Group Ltd;
- Rees,W (1991) *The Skills of Management*. London: Routledge;
- Sparrow, P and Hilthrop, J (1994) *Human Resource Management in Transition*. London: Prentice Hall;
- Sprenger, R (2002) *Hygiene for Management*. Doncaster: Highfield.co.uk Ltd;
- Code of Practice No.9: Food Hygiene Inspections (Second Revision October 2000) London: HMSO;
- Code of Practice No.19: Qualifications and Experience of Authorised Officers (Revised in December 2001) London: HMSO;
- Food Safety Act 1990. London: HMSO;
- Food Safety (General Food Hygiene) Regulations 1995. London: HMSO;
- Food Standards Act 1999. London: HMSO;
- Industry Guide to Good Hygiene Practice: Catering Guide (1997). London: Chadwick House Group Ltd;
- Industry Guide to Good Hygiene Practice: Retail Guide (1997). London: Chadwick House Group Ltd;
- IFST (1992) *Food Hygiene training: A guide to its responsible management*. London: Institute of Food Science and Technology;
- Leach, J (2002) A guide to customer perceptions of food hygiene. London: Chadwick House Group Ltd; and
- WHO Consultation Technical Report Series (1989), *Health surveillance and management procedures for food handling personnel*. Geneva: World Health Organisation.

4 Education and Training

"To learn, you must want to be taught." (Proverbs 2:1)

Question: In terms of food poisoning which is the most dangerous part of the human anatomy? Is it: a) Hands, b) Skin), c) Bowels, d) Nose?

Answer: All these are dangerous, but you may sensibly have chosen another option – the Brain.

Consider these

♦ School children undertake a Foundation Certificate in Food Hygiene course and examination as part on a GNVQ or GSCE programme.

♦ A food handler undertakes a Foundation Certificate in Food Hygiene course and examination to provide underpinning knowledge for an NVQ in food preparation.

♦ A food handler attends a Foundation Certificate in Food Hygiene course and receives a certificate, but no further supervision or instruction.

♦ A food handler fails an examination for a Foundation Certificate in Food Hygiene but has shown a marked improvement in practices and personal hygiene since attending the course.

Who, therefore, has received an education and who has received training? By reading the whole of this book, and some of the suggested titles in the reading lists at the end of each chapter, or visiting some of the suggested websites, in addition to putting some plan of action or commitment into practice, you may well come up with an answer! Perhaps the title of this chapter or even the title of this book should be Food Hygiene Learning. But for now accept the chosen title and read on.

Perhaps the most valuable result of all food hygiene training is the ability to make the food handler do the things they have to do, when it ought to be done, whether they like it or not. It is the first lesson that ought to be learned. "A little learning is not a dangerous thing to one who does not mistake it for a great deal"(William Allen White). If a food handler receives a certificate after passing a food hygiene examination today and stops learning tomorrow s/he will become uneducated the day after. Training is a continuous process that must be updated according to business and individual needs.

Key definitions
Education

A process and a series of activities, which aim at enabling an individual to assimilate and develop knowledge, skills, values and understanding, that are not simply related to a narrow field of activity, but allow a broad range of problems to be analysed and solved (Buckle, R and Caple, J, 1992).

Develop
To unfold more fully, bring out all that is potentially contained within.

Development
The growth or realisation of a person's ability, through conscious or unconscious learning (as defined by Manpower Services Commission 1981).

Employee development
The skilful provision and organisation of learning experiences and opportunities in the workplace in order that performance can be improved, that work goals can be achieved and that, through enhancing the skills, knowledge, learning ability and enthusiasm of people at every level, there can be continuous organisational as well as individual growth. Employee development must therefore be part of the wider strategy for the business, aligned with the organisation's corporate mission and goals (Harrison, R, 1992).

Knowledge
Understanding and information.

Learning
A change in behaviour.

Strategy
Put simply, this can be defined as "our plan of action and how it is to be carried out".

Train
To instruct and discipline in or for some particular occupation, trade, art or profession.

Training
A planned and systematic effort to modify or develop knowledge/skills/attitudes through learning experience, to achieve effective performance in an activity or range of activities. Its purpose, in the work situation, is to enable an individual to acquire abilities to adequately perform a given task (Buckle, R and Caple, J,1992).

Education and training differences

Education of food handlers has a major role to play by identifying the "potential" that appropriate education and training will have to offer for the maintenance of food safety. In 1985, the European Office of the WHO defined a number of health targets for Europe which were to be achieved by 2000. These targets were to meet WHO's global challenge to achieve for everyone a level of health which would permit them to lead a socially and economically productive life. One of the targets to be met was that there should be education and motivation to encourage people to improve and maintain health. This included improvement in food handling practices and reduction of food poisoning. Food hygiene education is not food hygiene training. For the former an individual may learn enough to help improve their understanding in another topic such as an NVQ, or in school as part of, for instance, a healthy eating week. Food Hygiene training, if carried out properly, becomes a skill which can be applied along side other food related activities, such as bar work, ancillary healthcare, or store work. It is therefore necessary to concentrate on training and consider it in discussions about the development of food handlers.

Using the key definitions, education and training are different. But they can be beneficial to each other.

For education these are:
♦ objectives are less specific than those used in training;
♦ educational plans take longer (a number of months or years, compared to, say one day for a training plan);
♦ methods and content do not extend to practical application and everyday use; and
♦ it is not usually associated with workplace development of employees, as it is with training.

This beneficial link of training and education may be summed up as "learning". All training involves some education. Combined with knowledge, understanding and practical implementation the outcome will be identifiable behavioural change. But this behavioural change needs nurturing in the form of planned development.

Who needs education and training?

Within the food and hospitality industries there are individuals who will need training and education throughout their working lives. This issue was discussed in more detail in an earlier chapter, "Who needs training?".

The Joint Food and Agricultural Organisation and WHO Food Standards Programme produced a recommended international code of practice in 1985 (FAO/WHO Codex Alimentarius, Volume A [1985] Recommended International Code of Practice General Principles of Food Hygiene, Geneva). Section IV (6.1) states: "Managers of Establishments should arrange for adequate and continuing training of all food handlers in hygienic handling of food and in personal hygiene so that they understand the precautions necessary to prevent contamination of food. Instructions should include all relevant parts of this Code." On 14 June 1993, the Council of European Communities issued a Directive (93/43/EEC) concerned with the Hygiene of Foodstuffs. Schedule X of the Directive stated "Food business operators shall ensure that food handlers are supervised and instructed and/or trained on food hygiene matters commensurate with their work activity." Almost all this wording was used to form the training regulation which is now in Schedule 1, Chapter X of the Food Safety (General Food Hygiene) Regulations 1995.

All food handlers need to be trained, for example, in handwashing and the part it has to play in preventing cross-contamination. A typical classroom-based course may discuss the whys and wherefores of handwashing, the occasions on which hands should be washed, and where they should be washed. As an inspecting officer for a local authority, the author has come across:
♦ managers who consider handwashing is a waste of time;
♦ managers who enter kitchens and never wash their hands;
♦ staff who have never been shown how to wash or dry hands properly;
♦ wash-hand basins without hot water, soap, or a means of drying hands;
♦ staff who are shouted at because they have not washed their hands;
♦ food preparation sinks used to wash hands;
♦ wash-hand basins which are wholly inaccessible because of location; and
♦ wash-hand basins used for food equipment storage.

When the food handlers have been on their courses they may learn about which parts of the hands and fingers need careful washing, and how the nails should be washed, etc. But, on returning to their premises, who actually supervises the food handlers in proper handwashing skills?

Identification of training needs

Training and development clearly do have a role to play as far as food handlers are concerned. However, training and development must be properly organised for them to be effective. Training must be closely linked to an organisation's strategic and business plans with clearly defined objectives, goals and targets.

Factors affecting training and development needs include:

♦ legislation (i.e. food hygiene training requirements);
♦ size and style of operation (e.g. fast food or cook-chill);
♦ customer type;
♦ business objectives and strategies;
♦ recruitment priorities; and
♦ budget and costs.

Other, more complex factors that ought to be taken into account include economic and social trends, political stability, and the commitment the organisation has to investing in its workforce.

Research into the training and qualifications held by unit managers working in contract catering companies in 1993 showed that 84% had City and Guilds, 57% possessed food hygiene qualifications, and 6% possessed some form of management qualification. When the respondents were asked to identify training priorities for their businesses, formal food hygiene training came top of the list, followed by team-building, training skills, supervisory skills, sales and marketing. When asked to report their individual training needs food hygiene training came first (Roberts, 1993) .

Businesses in catering often use a mix of methods to identify training and development activities. These include:

♦ analysis of strategic planned objectives;
♦ training needs audit;
♦ analysis of customer feedback;
♦ analysis of individual, team, department, unit and company performance;
♦ competitor analysis; and
♦ appraisal and performance review.

This last point, appraisal and performance review, has helped with deciding which type of Foundation Certificate in Food Hygiene course to send staff on (CIEH, RIPH, RSPH, and REHIS), which type of end of course exam they should sit (oral or written), or even if a more specialist course involving hazard analysis (see the table on page 113 for details).

Identifying the training and development needs can also involve training audits. These are useful for:

♦ smaller or independent companies who have not developed a training culture or infrastructure;

- when companies are expanding rapidly;
- development of a new company where large numbers of staff need to be trained;
- when existing companies need to review staff; and
- when larger companies restructure.

Individuals will need appraisals and reviews. These are concerned with:
- regular and systematic reviews of tasks undertaken;
- projections of future responsibilities and tasks;
- identifying individual training and development needs;
- identifying commercial needs; and
- equality of access and involvement.

Such schemes may in addition relate to pay, promotion, counselling, objective setting, etc. Time spent on identifying training needs and development can save a business much time and effort in the long run. Companies which offer basic food hygiene training as a work-based course, rather than in a theoretical context, offer the trainees a better chance of understanding and a greater sense of importance. The company can also ensure that staff are trained according to the specific needs of the organisation rather than generalised training.

Training and development plans

Whichever system is used to identify training and development needs, there is the need for a mechanism to achieve the desired outcome. This is most commonly satisfied by the design of a training plan that details the process by which the training will take place.

Training plans will differ depending upon the size and style of the company or business. Additionally, the format and size will vary dependent upon the number of staff involved. In a survey of 250 company training activities and plans (Roberts,1993) all identified preferences in respect of training:
- 70% favoured in-house courses;
- 65% identified the months of January and February as the best time for external training;
- 72% stated that their preferred training days were on Tuesday and Wednesday; and
- 80% favoured short courses in preference to the more normal traditional time-consuming certificated courses.

When developing a training plan in a food business food hygiene training must be included. This is because of the legal requirement specified in food safety regulations. The majority of employees will accept such training as both necessary and personally beneficial. It is worth noting that this is not always the case with other forms of training when employees are not told the reasons for attending.

An Investors in People (IiP) award involves the training and development of individuals on recruitment and throughout their employment. Any training development involvement needed to achieve the award should "focus on the needs of the all new recruits and continually develop and improve the skills of existing employees. All employees should be encouraged to contribute to identifying and meeting their needs and their own job-related needs". (IiP 1994). IiP is a good way to continually review development of training plans for all employees. The resource for the training and development of employees needs to be clearly identified in the business plan.

Development of training plans is dependent upon the effectiveness of systems for identifying needs and the ability of the organisation, company or business to design, resource, deliver, monitor, evaluate and adapt its plan. Such plans will have greater chances of success when employees are involved at the development stage. It is unfortunate that there is no national standard that is attractive enough to (and achievable for) independently run small catering or hotel businesses.

Even if businesses do not go in for IiP, development of effective training plans should include a degree of flexibility, and allow for adaptation or amendment. This last point is of particular relevance to those who were involved in the development of training for food handlers. In 1990, Section 26 of the Food Safety Act made provision for the introduction of food hygiene training regulations. Section 21 of the Food Safety Act 1990 provides proprietors of food businesses with a defence of due diligence to show that they have taken all reasonable precautions in avoiding committing any offence under the Act. This seemed to imply that food hygiene training was important. The first of three consultative documents regarding food hygiene training was issued by the Department of Health. On learning that training was to become a statutory requirement in the Food Safety (General Hygiene) Regulations **1994**, catering businesses and others employing food handlers were convinced that the basic food hygiene certificate was required as a basic minimum qualification. Enforcement agencies and training organisations contributed towards the confusion. It was not until the Food Safety (General Food Hygiene) Regulations **1995** came into force on 15 September 1995 that it became clear that a Foundation food hygiene certificate was not required by food handlers. Unfortunately trainers, managers and enforcement officers misinterpreted the legal wording and what was really required.

Training plans in businesses are increasingly making provision for supervisors or managers to become the food hygiene trainers rather than using external organisations. However, if the training plan is developed it is important to realise individuals learn at different paces and will respond differently to specific training methods. Trainers, managers, and enforcement officers now have to ask themselves if "a certificate course is best for the business or food handler, or would on-site practical job specific training be more effective?"

Reducing the effectiveness of training and education of food handlers

There are situations which can damage or reduce the effectiveness of any training or education programme. These could include:

- publicising new proposed training requirements and encouraging businesses to "jump on the band wagon";
- consultants, trainers and enforcement officers delivering mistruths and misconceptions about training requirements;
- training being under-valued by proprietors and employees;
- legal and paperwork fatigue by businesses;
- lack of decent training facilities and trainers; and
- culture of an organisation.

Design, delivery and evaluation of training and development

Training and development plans are also discussed in the chapter "Who needs training?" Training centres around what employees will need to learn to enable them to perform their work. Development concerns what they will need in the future to keep them up-to-date, stop complacency and bad habits, help to keep them motivated and the opportunities for promotion or more responsibility. The design of training and development is concerned with the identification of:

- the required outcome and benefits;
- methods and approaches to training;
- the range of employees, target groups and individuals;
- the programming and scheduling; and
- communicating the availability and range of programmes to employers/ees and the creation of systems which help the activity take place.

The design of the training programme will have to include content, method, timing, administration, registration, purpose etc. Managers and trainers face an uphill task of getting the balance right if education and training are to be really effective. Training and development can be major expenses for many small businesses especially if there is a high turnover of staff. Just have a look at the figures below regarding the make-up of the hospitality and catering sector in the UK.

One in three workers are porters or catering assistants.

- 14% of chefs and cooks are from minority ethnic backgrounds;
- at least 30% of catering posts are part-time; and
- 13% of caterers will use their current posts as a stop gap before finding another job.

Source: Labour Market Review 2002: Hospitality Network Newsflash , issue 26 June 2002

Owners of food businesses want training and development to be successful, with a quality outcome and with minimal of disruption to normal operating conditions, otherwise the investment will be wasted. Key elements in a training and development culture include:

- short and long term investment for the development and training of individuals and businesses;
- placing emphasis on communication and participation;
- implementation of management systems that influence the requirement for total employee involvement and implementation of effective control measures;
- identification and problem solving through a team approach; and
- social inclusion and equal opportunities for all employees.

The National Council for Vocational Qualifications has identified the key purpose of training and development as "to develop human potential to assist organisations and individuals to achieve their objectives. Without a culture in the business the objectives will never be properly be achieved."

According to Dr D. Rennie, in her paper 'Health Education Models and Food Hygiene Education' (published in The Royal Society for the Promotion of Health Journal dated April 1995): "Food hygiene training is an example of the application of the cognitive approach to education, in which it is expected that the provision of relevant information, or knowledge, will lead to change in practice." The Foundation Certificate in Food Hygiene courses should involve the use of systematic and planned training approaches. But are these courses "training"? Perhaps partially, but more realistically they are "education". Experience has shown that too many employees attend the certificate courses and do not get any help, encouragement or supervision with putting what they have been taught into practice. According to the Institute of Food Science and Technology, in their booklet entitled "Food Hygiene Training: A guide to responsible management (1992)", courses should include core topics common to all food businesses, and topics particularly relevant to the type of food business and to the foods being handled in that business.

Benefits of training

"I can educate people, but I cannot make them learn", or to misquote Socrates, "I can train people, but I cannot make them learn."

A structured approach to training will enable organisations and businesses to obtain maximum benefits. The benefits of proper food hygiene training have been recognised for decades. Until the mid-1990s it had been left up to the discretion of proprietors of food businesses whether or not employees were to be sent on recognised courses. Prior to 1982 no formal certificate courses really existed. One of the first food hygiene handbooks to be written for food handlers was by Richard Sprenger of Highfield.co.uk Ltd. He also put forward the idea for formalising courses. In the 1980s various examination bodies jumped on the band wagon and used the chapters in the handbook as syllabus headings, under which were written aims and objectives. Many of the national food hygiene certificate course syllabuses have not changed to meet the needs of employees and their employers; instead they provide more of a generic course programme. Since 1995, food hygiene training and/or instruction and supervision have been on the statute books. Unfortunately too many employers and enforcement officers have seen training just in terms of attending a nationally recognised course and not - as should have been done long ago – persuading Central Government that pre-course practice assessments and post-course behavioural change assessments are required. Small businesses may rely heavily on an external trainer without giving much consideration to what the employees are going to do or need once they have attended the courses.

In terms of food hygiene the benefits to the business if proper training is carried out include:
- decrease in customer complaints;
- increased staff motivation;
- reduction in waste;
- lower staff turnover; and
- legal compliance, etc.

For the food handler proper training means:
- promotion prospects;
- nationally recognised qualification;
- a sense of purpose;
- pride in their work; and
- becoming part of a team.

These are discussed in more detail elsewhere in this book. However, it must be emphasised that many businesses, both large and small, have run their own successful in-house training programmes without relying on an accredited examination body. There are a whole range of reasons for this:

♦ no course to meet their needs;
♦ a defined and workable training strategy;
♦ certification of in-house programmes by organisations such as the RIPH;
♦ to cut down the expense of examination and registration fees;
♦ use of one-to-one or on-the-job training;
♦ promoting ownership of food hygiene by staff; and
♦ dissatisfaction with type and content of examinations.

A successful training programme will involve:

♦ management of the training programme;
♦ workforce assessment;
♦ establishing a training committee;
♦ careful design of the content of the training programmes;
♦ the location and timing of training sessions;
♦ visual aids and equipment;
♦ piloting the programme;
♦ pre-course assessment;
♦ implementation of the training programme;
♦ evaluation of the programme;
♦ post-course practical instruction and supervision; and
♦ reinforcement of the programme.

Just consider some of the effects of a badly managed food hygiene training programme on a business and its employees:

♦ no encouragement for employees to put into practice what they have been taught;
♦ practices remain the same as before training;
♦ irrelevant course content which does not meet the needs of the business or employees;
♦ employer does not explain to employees why they are being trained and what will happen after the course; and
♦ management will not let staff put into practice what they have been taught.

The cost of training food handlers

A report published by Her Majesty's Stationery Office (HMSO) entitled "Department of Health Compliance Cost Assessment: Food Safety (General Food Hygiene) Regulations 1994" indicated that the food industry training requirement would lead to more innovative training. Food hygiene training would cost the industry £35 to £42 million, which represents about 15% of the industry's total training bill. Given that the industry is facing a high turnover of employees it is easy to see why alternative means of training are being sourced – especially as the traditional certificate based courses no longer meet the needs of specific sectors within the UK's food industry.

It is not only financial considerations which have to be taken into account. Other constraints include:

♦ the need for operators to change priorities at short notice;

♦ the ability of a business to implement all its plans because of operational factors;
♦ unplanned staff shortages due to illness or change of shifts; and
♦ determination of the effectiveness of training plans and activities.

What does training involve?

It should be clear that a classroom-based course, or a course which is only intended to get a candidate through an examination, is clearly not "training", or certainly, and more correctly, not complete training. The situation is compounded by the difficulty that food safety legislation has no legal definition of "training". A simple definition of training is a practical application of theory gained through knowledge and an understanding of a specific subject to enable an individual to perform a specific function. Dictionaries have various definitions based on this example.

Take a look at the variety of training methods available:

For food handlers on their own:
♦ reading;
♦ revision;
♦ watching a training video;
♦ computer based training or e-Learning; and
♦ distance or open book learning.

A collection of people in one room at the same time as a group, such as a kitchen brigade or trainees from different organisations attending a common event:
♦ training room, classroom, lectures;
♦ meetings, discussions;
♦ combined projects;
♦ workshops;
♦ case studies; and
♦ seminars, conferences, forums.

Work-based training (on-the-job):
♦ practical instruction;
♦ supervision and coaching;
♦ practical application; and
♦ supervisory or managerial activities.

Competency assessment must follow the training

For the training to have any use at all, competency assessment of the food handlers who have undertaken training must be achieved. Refer to the chapter in this book about "Competency or Certification?"

So how do people learn?

According to Plutarch, "Democritus said, words are but the shadows of actions." Janwillem van de Wetering in a book called "The Empty Mirror" gives an example of someone trying to explain learning: The master shook his head. "I could answer your questions, but I won't try because you won't understand the answer… Imagine that I am holding a pot of tea and you are thirsty. You want me to give you a cup of tea. I can pour tea but you will have to produce a cup. I can't pour the tea on your hands or you will get burnt. If I pour it on to the floor I will spoil the floor mats. You have to have a cup. That cup will form in yourself by the training you will receive here."

For learning to be successful it must be:
♦   enjoyable and able to maintain interest;
♦   highly participative for the employees;
♦   understandable for the employees no matter what their culture or language ability;
♦   up-to-date and accurately presented, with evidence to support facts or statements;
♦   at a time to suit the employees and their business; and
♦   on-going throughout an individual's working life and beyond.

A range of social cognition models influence people. These models demonstrate how their environment may affect people, what they already know and what they feel about it, and what other people do. Neuro-linguistic programming (NLP) is the study of human excellence. The three parts of NLP may be summarised as follows:

♦   Neuro – this looks at the way we interact and communicate, plus brain patterns. For instance, if explaining a colour-coded chopping board to an employee they will get far more out of the session by being allowed to use the board, rather than just being told about one without being shown a picture or being able to hold an example.

♦   Linguistic – This is seeing and hearing at the same time. If two food handlers in the same room are doing one of each they will not be able to communicate with each other. So feedback and encouraging trainees to ask questions, in addition to working out solutions for themselves will improve communication.

♦   Programming – Motivation and focusing upon good, rather than bad, practices will help individuals believe in themselves and that they have a positive contribution to make. It does not make sense for a manager to shout at a food handler when something goes wrong. It would be best to encourage the food handler to look at what went well and then for them to make contributions or get involved in how things can be put right.

Various models have been designed to explain the process of training and abilities to learn. Whilst this book veers away from academia and technicalities a couple of examples of models may help to summarise where we have got to so far.

MODEL ONE:

Learning (power of understanding)
⇩
Attitude (feelings regarding something)
⇩
Behaviour (a way of conducting oneself)
⇩
Competency (adequate knowledge to be able to perform properly)

MODEL TWO:

If food hygiene/safety training is to be effective –

There must be accurate and relevant knowledge of food safety
⇩
Learning must be designed to motivate and stimulate employees
⇩
Organisations must encourage employees to put their learning into practice
⇩
Each employee should be able to turn theory into practice within their workplace
⇩
Organisations must strive for continual improvement in cost-effective hygiene measures

How SMART is the training?

All training sessions should meet the ability and needs of the students. Careful planning is necessary to ensure that candidates do not feel excluded during any training session. If choosing a trainer or training provider it will be necessary to identify programmes with objectives that are:

Specific
Measurable
Achievable
Realistic
Time bound

♦ **S**pecific: Decide what has to be put across and what the trainees already know. It must be relevant to the objective. For example trainees need to know how to use a probe thermometer and how to record temperatures of food freshly taken out of a microwave oven.

♦ **M**easurable: Determine how the success is to be measured, for example, the use of senses. After an explanation and demonstration encourage the trainees to practise taking temperatures of freshly microwaved foods with a probe thermometer and ensure that the results are accurately recorded.

♦ **A**chievable: Ensure that what has to be put across can be done in the time that it has to be done, and that the target audience have the ability to achieve it. In the case of the example used, the training session is 45 minutes. (Five minutes for the introduction, ten minutes for an explanation and demonstration, 20 minutes for practice by the trainees, and the remainder for conclusion, questions, etc.)

♦ **R**ealistic: Trainees need to be taught about issues which are relevant to their work and shown materials or set targets to which they can relate. Use probe thermometers, record books, and microwave ovens with which the trainees are familiar.

♦ **T**ime bound: Practice makes perfect! Training sessions are run for specific time periods. Know how long the each period is and stick to it, i.e. in this example, 45 minutes.

WHERE TO FIND TRAINERS

Local authorities	Try Yellow pages or your local telephone directory.	www.tagish.co.uk/
Colleges of further and higher education	Try Yellow pages or your local telephone directory, or a reference library.	www.hesa.ac.uk
The Royal Institute of Public Health	020 75810 2731	www.riph.org.uk
The Royal Society for the Promotion of Health	020 7630 0121	www.rshealth.org
The Chartered Institute of Environmental Health	020 7928 6006	www.cieh.org.uk
The Royal Environmental Health Institute of Scotland	0131 225 6999	www.rehis.org
Food Safety Consultants and Trainers Directory	020 7928 6006	www.ehn-online.com/services
Web sites		www.foodsafetytrainers.co.uk

Training providers

A range of organisations may register with accredited examination bodies to run food hygiene courses and to offer the examinations at the end of each course. These organisations include:

♦ in-house trainers;
♦ consultants;
♦ local authorities;
♦ distance learning or open learning providers;
♦ further and higher education establishments; and
♦ organisations on the internet.

Examples of where to find the trainers from above organisations include:

♦   internet, for example, www.foodsafetytrainers.co.uk
♦   examination bodies, as listed above;
♦   trade journals, such as Caterer and Hotelkeeper;
♦   "word of mouth"; and
♦   trade and professional associations.

Qualifications for a trainer

To be a trainer does not require any formal qualification if you do not run nationally recognised accredited courses. But a trainer must know their subject, keep up-to-date, and be able to justify what they are telling their audience.

The awarding bodies set criteria for prospective trainers. It is up to the reader to check with each awarding body for specific requirements. Generally, food safety and hygiene experience is necessary, plus a minimum qualification such as the Advanced Certificate in Food Hygiene, or a degree with the main subject being related to food studies. In addition, teaching and training qualifications are required, such as:

♦   CIEH Professional Trainers Certificate;
♦   Health Development Agency/Open University Health Education Certificate;
♦   City and Guilds Institute 7407 parts one and two, or other relevant awards;
♦   HCTC Group Training Techniques, Managing the Trainer Function, etc;
♦   University degrees, diplomas, or certificates in Education, Training, Health Promotion, etc;
♦   NVQs to Level III or IV in training and development; and
♦   Chartered Institute of Personnel Development Certificate in Training Practice, etc.

The oddity in all the requirements is that REHIS and CIEH do not require their corporate members (i.e. EHOs) to have any specific training qualifications. How can their competency be really assessed, say compared to a Health Education Officer who works in a food safety training team in a local authority? The latter will have to produce copies of all their certificates, plus details of about five years' relevant experience and the former will just have to give their membership number. Many EHOs and enforcement officers do make very good trainers – but it is normally those who believe that education and training have a justifiable role in enforcement of food safety legislation. Many of these go on to do masters degrees in food control or health promotion. The old school, of whom some still exist, show signs of trying to find excuses to ignore the fact that if laws are broken this is fault of the proprietor, rather than it may be due to a breakdown in understanding and communication between the enforcer and the business. As in many professions, there are also very good EHOs, but they do not feel comfortable about training or educating others.

Who monitors the educators and trainers?

There are a wide range of government agencies, charities and examination bodies concerned with ensuring that education and training meet the interests of the recipients and help to develop the best possible educational and training infrastructure for the UK. Examples below are primarily concerned with education and training in England and Wales. The reader is strongly advised to contact government agencies and authorities responsible for Scotland, and Northern Ireland for further information.

Department of Education and Skills:

In 2001 a new Department for Education and Skills (DfES) was established with the purpose of creating opportunity, releasing potential and achieving excellence for all. The Adult Learning Division of the Department for Education and Skills has a website devoted to accessible learning for over 19s. www.lifelonglearning.co.uk is perhaps the leading web site for the encouragement, promotion and development of lifelong learning. Read the chapter about e-Learning for further details of government funded e-Learning and computer based training initiatives. The DfES is responsible for the control of the QCA, Learning & Skills Council (LSC), Adult Learning Inspectorate (ALI) and the Learning Skills Development Agency (LSDA). All of these are summarised below.

QCA:

The Qualifications and Curriculum Authority (QCA) is at www.qca.org.uk. It is a guardian of standards in education and training. The QCA works with others to maintain and develop the school curriculum and associated assessments, and to accredit and monitor qualifications in schools, colleges and at work. It has developed with its partner regulatory authorities in Wales and Northern Ireland a coherent and transparent national framework of qualifications to guarantee quality and standards, meeting the full range of needs of learners and those who provide education, employment and training.

Its aims are to:

♦ widen participation and promote life-long learning;
♦ clarify the relationships between qualifications, including broad equivalences and routes of progression;
♦ facilitate choice and combination of qualification types, and breadth of study or specialism within a particular area where necessary for progression;
♦ allow reasonable choice and scope across different qualification types for innovation, whilst avoiding unnecessary overlap and duplication;
♦ command public and professional confidence in the qualifications system.

ALI:

The Adult Learning Inspectorate (ALI) is at www.ali.gov.uk. It was set up under the provision of the Learning and Skills Act 2000 to help create a new system of post-16 learning in this country, which is coherent and accessible and is responsive to the needs of individuals, businesses and communities. The ALI works with the Learning and Skills Council (LSC) and the Employment Service (ES) to, amongst other responsibilities, assist in the promotion of excellence in learning, raising the profile of lifelong learning, and improving the coherence and consistency of adult learning. It has also developed a Common Inspection Framework. Both the Chief Inspector of Schools and Chief Inspector of Adult Learning keep the Secretary of State informed about the quality of education and training; standards achieved by those receiving education and training and whether the education and training provide value for money. There are seven questions the inspections are guided by. These are:

1. How well do learners achieve?
2. How effective are teaching, training and learning?
3. How are achievement and learning affected by resources?
4. How effective are assessment and monitoring of learning?
5. How well do the programmes and courses meet the needs and interests of learners?

6. How well are the learners guided and supported?

7. How effective are leadership and management in raising achievement and supporting all learners?

A learner is a person receiving education or training, including student, trainee, apprentice, client, and participant. A teacher or trainer is someone responsible for teaching or training. It also includes lecturers, tutors, instructors, supervisors, technicians and assessors when they have a teaching or training function.

(Acknowledgement for this source of information is given to ALI and OFSTED)

Learning and Skills Council:

The Learning and Skills Council is responsible for funding and planning education and training for over 16-year-olds in England. Visit www.lsc.gov.uk. The LSC's mission is to raise participation and attainment through high-quality education and training which puts learners first. The Council operates through 47 local offices and a national office in Coventry.
The Learning and Skills Council are responsible for:

- ♦ further education;
- ♦ work-based training and young people;
- ♦ workforce development;
- ♦ adult and community learning;
- ♦ information, advice and guidance for adults; and
- ♦ education business links.

LSDA:

The Learning and Skills Development Agency (LSDA) (www.lsda.org.uk) is a strategic national resource for the development of policy and practice in post-16 education and training. The Agency was previously known as the Further Education Development Agency (FEDA).

NIACE:

The National Institute of Adult Continuing Education (NIACE) is a registered charity. The strategic plan of NIACE is to:

"support an increase in the total numbers of adults engaged in formal and informal learning in England and Wales; and at the same time to take positive action to improve opportunities and widen access to learning opportunities for those communities under-represented in current provision."

It is a membership organisation, with individual members and more than 260 corporate members across the full range of providers, policy makers and users of adult learning opportunities. NIACE headquarters are in Leicester, England and Cardiff, Wales. NIACE is an England and Wales body (within Wales a specialist committee, NIACE Cymru, oversees the organisation's work). It works in all fields of UK education and training. NIACE has a particular concern for widening access to learning opportunities and increasing participation among those groups currently under-represented in education and training.

LVSTC

The London Voluntary Sector Skills Training Consortium (LVSTC) was legally incorporated as a charity in October 1989. Visit www.lvstc.org.uk for full details. It was established to:

♦ promote, and increase the amount of high quality voluntary sector training run by and for disadvantaged groups in London;

♦ increase funding available to London's voluntary sector training providers from Europe and elsewhere;

♦ promote partnership between voluntary sector providers and local authorities, colleges, LSCs, the EU, Government, the private sector and others to secure maximum European and other resources for economic regeneration programmes in London; and

♦ highlight issues of concern to voluntary sector providers, working with these groups in a democratic and accountable way.

Examination bodies:

Examination bodies have their own strict criteria for trainers and training centres who wish to run accredited food hygiene certificate courses. Monitoring of the quality of trainers by the examination bodies is variable. Some poor trainers may go unchecked by awarding bodies. But some do impose set conditions to run accredited food hygiene certificate courses. For instance the CIEH expects its registered trainers to sign up to a Trainer's Charter. This charter has seven key principles to ensure trainers maintain a high standard of delivery which serve the needs of trainees. For further information visit www.cieh.org.uk

In Scotland:
Enterprise and lifelong learning department

The Enterprise and Lifelong Learning Department (ELLD) supports Scottish Ministers in developing and promoting an environment that encourages business and enterprise to flourish in Scotland.

♦ schemes to support innovation, and lists other events.

Enterprise network

The Scottish Executive's economic development and skills objectives are promoted in collaboration with Scottish Enterprise and Highlands & Islands Enterprise through a network of Local Enterprise Companies (LECs). LECs provide support to business start-ups, venture capital, and a range of business services. The LECs also deliver training programmes, including Youth Training and Skillseekers/Modern Apprenticeships for young people, and Training for Work for unemployed adults. Further information on the involvement of ELLD with the Enterprise Network is available on the Enterprise Network information page at www.scotland.gov.uk/who/elld

Lifelong learning

ELLD promotes lifelong learning through policy development and funding for further and adult education, and higher education in Scotland. ELLD promotes and supports education and training for people at every stage in life beyond school age. We have established **learndirect** Scotland which continues to be successful in promoting any time, anywhere learning. It is now working with business to promote in-work learning through **learndirect**

Scotland for business.

The world of work is constantly evolving. We launched a new national all age guidance organisation, Careers Scotland, in April 2002. This has brought together the roles previously undertaken by the Careers Service Companies, Adult Guidance Networks, Education Business Partnerships and Local Learning Partnerships, offering clients a one-stop shop approach to careers support services.

ELLD also funds The Scottish Further Education Funding Council and The Scottish Higher Education Funding Council which are responsible for financing Scotland's Universities, and the higher and further education (FE) institutions.

(This section is copied with acknowledgement to the Scottish Office)

In Northern Ireland

Visit www.niassembly.gov.uk to establish what is happening to adult training and education in Northern Ireland.

Conclusion

Training, education and development of food handlers will continue to have a vital role especially where food hygiene and safety are concerned. Currently reliance on generic certificate courses means that too many food handlers are just being educated about food hygiene principles, rather than being given the chance to demonstrate practice. Training which provides work-based qualifications, proof of competence at work, employment-led, not tied to a specific route of learning, and available to everyone should be required in the near future. Moves are being made to put food hygiene as a "life skill" on the National Curriculum at primary and secondary level.

Further reading

- Buckle, R and Caple, J (1992) *The theory and practice of training*. Kogan Page;
- Harrison, R (1992), *Employee Development*, IPM;
- Institute of Food Science and Technology, (1992) *Food Hygiene Training: A guide to responsible management;*
- Rennie, D (1995) *Health Education Models and Food Hygiene Education,* The Royal Society for the Promotion of Health Journal, April 1995; and
- Roberts, J (1994) *Human Resource Practice in the Hospitality Industry*. London: Hodder and Stoughton.

5 Barriers to Overcome

"I have striven not to laugh at human actions, not to weep at them, nor to hate them, but to understand them." (Baruch Spinoza 1632-1677)

Barriers? What barriers?

A feeling of well-being usually pre-disposes energy and positive attitude. The WHO defines health as follows: "physical, social, and mental well-being not merely the absence of disease or injury." Taking this into account, many factors affect an individual's health, and therefore their attitude, response and commitment towards learning. No matter how well motivated a food handler is, a negative attitude may result from a previously unhelpful teaching or training experience.

Trainers, enforcement officers, managers and supervisors must accept that food handlers need motivating if they are to make a positive contribution to food safety.

Well motivated staff will bring out their talents and, with careful nurturing, develop an eagerness to learn. They may work at their own pace, and that may have some effect on the way the business operates. A poor manager or supervisor is one who fails to accept that language, learning difficulties or special needs may be barriers which prevent the contribution to food safety being made.

Some food handlers are better than others at putting what they have been taught into practice. It is conceivable that a food handler can demonstrate good hygiene practices and at the same time fail a certificate examination. Failure does not make him/her a bad food handler or someone who has not complied with the law. Competency manifests itself in many forms. The candidate who flies through the examinations may not be able to convert the theory into practice. This individual may actually pose more of a risk to food safety within the business than the individual who failed the examination. A skilled trainer will help to find a balance.

The barriers to overcome are:
- lack of basic skills;
- disability discrimination;
- special needs;
- learning difficulties;
- language;
- diversity in ethnic backgrounds;
- social class diversity;
- different cultural and/or religious beliefs;
- different values;
- gender issues; and
- age discrimination.

Basic skills

Basic skills means "the ability to read, write and speak in English, use mathematics at a level necessary to function and progress at work and society in general." It does not necessarily include learning difficulties, English for Speakers of Other Languages (ESOL), or Special Needs. Approximately 20% of the adult population in the UK are not functionally literate. Far more have problems with numbers. Trainees and their employers may not be aware that help is to hand. The problem in food hygiene matters will only come to light, for example, if a food handler cannot read storage instructions on food labelling or interpret cooking times. A food business needs to ensure that its environment is welcoming and creates a climate that puts people at their ease. The benefits connected with encouraging a feeling of belonging, use of facilities, and timetabling. These may have an influence on someone who works shifts or part-time.

Each individual will have different influences and pressures placed upon them throughout life. As a result their attitude and motivation can be for or against specific behaviour. Before attending any food hygiene training some consideration must be given to the individual's background and preconceptions of learning. Their age and achievement at school may act as barriers to learning. Cultural and religious barriers can be strong and difficult for individuals to overcome. For instance, some Muslim Moroccans cannot be taught by a male teacher or with other men in the room.

Disability discrimination

Managers who fail to recognise disability which prevents a food handler from gaining a qualification and managing with traditional training techniques may fall foul of the Disability Discrimination Act 1995. Disabilities and other barriers to learning may be overcome with careful planning, consideration and an understanding of the trainee's individual needs.

The Office for Population Census Survey estimates that approximately 6.5 million people in Britain are disabled. 1 in 6 people may experience some form of disability in their lifetime. 11% of the working population are disabled. 23% of people become disabled through their work activities. The charities connected with a range of disabilities estimate that in the UK there are:

- 1 million blind and visually impaired people;
- 4% of visually impaired people have no sight;
- 10% of the population have dyslexia;
- 20% of employees will experience mental health difficulties; and
- 2% of the population have a learning disability.

The Disability Discrimination Act 1995 defines a "disabled person" as a person with "a physical or mental impairment which has a substantial and long term adverse effect on his ability to carry out normal day to day activities." For more details about the legislation visit the Disability Rights Commission web-site at www.drc-gb.org.

A registered disabled person may be treated as disabled for the purposes of the Act. A person may be suffering from the effects of physical or mental impairment. An effect which is more than minor or trivial may be regarded as substantial. Employers will need to assess how an impairment prevents a person from carrying out a generally accepted method of doing something in their course of work. Behaviour may be affected when, for instance, a dyslexic person cannot cope when being put under stress. An example of this is being given a multiple choice tick test examination. The person concerned may however be perfectly able to demonstrate good food hygiene practice in a work situation. Environmental factors such as light, shade, glare, heat, cold, and humidity, may also have an effect.

Normal day-to-day activities can affect a person's ability with task performance. One of the following may be affected:

- Mobility – for example, taking something out of a freezer cabinet;

- Manual dexterity – using a probe thermometer;
- Physical co-ordination – for example, holding a piece of fish and de-boning it;
- Continence – involuntary urination or defaecation;
- Ability to lift, carry or otherwise move everyday objects – for example, stock rotation;
- Speech – for example, inability to clearly inform a supervisor about faulty equipment;
- Hearing – for example, not being able to hear instructions or a trainer;
- Eyesight – for example, affected by colour blindness or shortsightedness;
- Memory or inability to concentrate, learn or understand – for example, short attention span or failure to sit in a training room for more than an hour a day; and
- Perception of the risk of physical danger – for example, knife handling or using cleaning chemicals.

Disability therefore concerns much more than a person being in a wheelchair. It includes physical, sensory, specific learning difficulties (for example, dyslexia), mental health needs and hidden disabilities such as diabetes, asthma, and epilepsy. Further advice may be gained from:

- The Employers' Forum on Disability publishes a Disability Communication Guide. Employers may find this useful when considering the food safety training needs of a new or existing employee. Visit www.employers-forum.co.uk

- The British Dyslexia Association provides advice about employing people with dyslexia. Telephone 0118 966 8271or visit www.bda-dyslexia.org.uk

- MIND produce publications to help employers who employ staff with mental health needs. Telephone 020 8519 2122 or visit www.mind.org.uk

- The Royal National Institute for the Blind have a special web-site to help employers with specific queries which they may have in connection with training services, recruitment and retention and useful contacts. Telephone 020 7388 1266 or visit www.rnib.org.uk.

- The Royal National Institute for Deaf People (RNID) has a web-site with support, advice and contacts fully listed. Telephone 0808 808 0123 (freephone) or visit www.rnid.org.uk

Special needs

All food premises should have a special needs policy - not just in consideration of the customers - but to enable effective training of food handlers who have distinct special needs. Sometimes food handlers may appear very bright, but are inhibited or frustrated by having an unrecognised learning difficulty. Choosing a training programme for one individual may not be suitable for another. Colleges of Adult Education and the examination bodies can provide support and guidance for both managers and trainees. As an example: for some years the two types of assessment available for candidates undertaking a Foundation Certificate in Food Hygiene course have been either a multi-choice or an oral examination. These methods of assessment may not be suitable for all trainees. For people with learning difficulties and disabilities, practical training with continuous work-based assessment of competence can be a more suitable route, such as the Wigan and Leigh College programme. Recognising the need for such a programme, the CIEH has given its support to competence-based assessment as an alternative to the traditional forms of assessment.

Learning difficulties

A food handler may have learning difficulties if s/he:

- has a significantly greater difficulty in learning than the majority of others of the same age; and
- has a disability which hinders or prevents him/her from making use of the training facilities generally provided for other food handlers.

A food handler must not be regarded as having a learning difficulty only because the language or form of language of their community or home is a different language from that in which·they are being taught.

Learning difficulties, special needs and the law

Under Section 2 of the Health and Safety at Work Act (HSWA), every employer has a duty to ensure, as far as reasonably practicable, the health safety and welfare at work of all his employees. In addition, the employer must provide information, instruction, training and supervision as is necessary to ensure, so far as is reasonably practicable, a safe system of work. There is no legal definition of information, instruction and training. The Management of Health and Safety at Work Regulations (MHSWR) 1999 place general duties on employers to provide information, instruction and training in order to ensure health and safety. The Approved Code of Practice (ACOP) for these regulations is well worth reading concerning guidance for training and instructing employees who may have language problem or special needs.

Although the Food Safety Act 1990 is the primary piece of legislation enforced for activities which may affect food safety in food premises, the HSWA concerns workplace safety in food premises and other businesses. However, the guidance and interpretation of the former and its provisions are very vague and unhelpful. The enforcement authorities and the Employment Medical Advisory Service may be able to give further guidance where training and instruction difficulties arise because of learning difficulties and special needs.

The Local Government Act 2000 places a duty on local authorities to "prepare community strategies for promoting or improving the economic, social and environmental wellbeing of their areas, and contributing to the achievement of sustainable development in the UK".

ESOL food handlers

Food handlers who speak little or no English as a second language are on the increase in the UK's hotel and catering industry. This is due to migrant workers, settled communities, refugees, and partners from all over the world.

The English Speaking Board is an examination board offering graded syllabuses and assessments for pupils and adults. The Founder and President of the board is on record as saying:

"Oral language is man's tool with which he makes friends, earns a living and becomes a participating member of the community. It is through speech that we assimilate thoughts, opinions, ideas, emotions, humour, wisdom, common sense, morals and spiritual values of those around us. It is through perceptive listening and courteous speaking that we move towards breaking down social, professional and racial barriers."

Trainers, managers and employees would do well to make use of local authority adult education services if they require further information about language development services, and also for assessments of English as a second language. The internet has a wealth of information as well. There are four fluency areas which need to be considered:

◆ writing;
◆ reading;
◆ speaking; and
◆ listening.

The assessed stages of ability may be summarised as:

◆ Stage 1 No English language Skills
◆ Stage 2 Basic
◆ Stage 3 Intermediate
◆ Stage 4 Fully fluent in English
◆ Stage 5 Speaks, reads, or writes English as a first language.

Train a food handler in the wrong language, give him/her an examination paper in a language that cannot be understood, fail to recognise their culture or experience and the trainer or manager will be heading towards alienating a potentially useful member of the food business. It would be wrong to assume that all food handlers can sit through a food hygiene course run in English and be expected to pass an examination with words for which they have no direct translation (such as gravy, elderly, spore or hazard). Likewise, talking about pork for one community or, for example, mackerel pâté for a community which is in a part of the world where mackerel does not exist, will not do anything to break down the barriers mentioned by the Board's founder.

The manager and trainer will need to consider each individual's ability and needs. For instance food handlers from different backgrounds and cultures will have considerably different needs depending upon their education, language skills, work experience in their own country, aptitude for learning and their age.

There is a national shortage of registered trainers to help non-English-speaking food handlers. Learning environments may be hostile or patronising with a culturally insensitive curriculum. The problematical wording of the questions in foundation and intermediate level food hygiene examinations for non-English-speaking food handlers, together with the lack of language trainers, requires help from the examination bodies and industry representatives. Furthermore, the FSA could provide assistance to non-English-speaking food handlers at a national level.

An industry priority?

The wide range of posts and variable patterns of work within the hospitality industry mean that a diverse range of people may be attracted. An increasing number of the posts are part time and attract people who may not speak English as a first language, have basic skills needs or may be socially included within their work place or community. In 2002, on behalf of the Department for Education and Skills Adult Basic Skills Strategy Unit, a survey of just over 400 employers identified:

◆ a lack of understanding of the term "basic skills". Over 40 percent thought it was to do with competencies relating to cooking or laying a table. Only 25% understood the term to mean literacy and numeracy skills;

- employers made no time to consider the basic skills needs of their employees, even at the interview stage;
- training and development to do the "job" were more important than development of basic skills; and
- the hospitality industry has a high percentage of employees who speak English as a foreign language. Employers tended to leave those who did not pick up English language skills in back of house dead-end positions such as cleaning, housekeeping or kitchen portering.

The language barrier in practice

The following extract is reproduced by kind permission of the RSPH. The original version of Euan MacAuslan's article first appeared in the Journal of the RSPH, December 2001, Vol 121, No 4, page 213 to 219.

The Royal Borough of Kensington and Chelsea, in London, is a major visitor destination being home to three of the most visited museums/galleries in the UK, and hosts the largest carnival in Europe in Notting Hill. Around 30,000 visitors stay in the Borough each night, and there are approximately 2000 registered food premises. Amongst the first migrant workers to settle in the Borough during the 1950s were Moroccans. They were recruited to work in London's hotels and restaurants. In the schools 70 different languages are spoken, and the 1991 Census revealed over 100 languages spoken amongst the adult population. 14,000 residents (8% of the total population) in the Borough work in the hotel and catering industry (not borough specific). 17,000 people work in the Borough's tourism and hospitality industry. 50% of these are part-time. 85% of the small businesses in the Borough employ less than 10 people. 25% of all jobs in the Borough are filled by local residents.

In 1999, The Directorate of Environmental Health undertook a survey of 488 independent restaurants and cafés to establish the most commonly spoken languages amongst food handlers apart from English. The survey established that 47 different languages other than English were spoken by food handlers in the premises. In descending order, the 8 most common languages were: Italian (33% of food handlers), French (31%), Spanish (30%), and Portuguese (30%). Others were Arabic, Turkish, Thai, and Tagalog. Since 2000, there has been an increase in Eastern European language-speaking candidates passing through the Council's foundation and intermediate courses. Businesses have a high turnover of hourly paid staff.

The only food handlers guaranteed to receive refresher training in The Borough are the 300 plus owners of food stalls who wish to apply for a trading licence at the Notting Hill Carnival. They have to undergo food hygiene training as part of their licence conditions. Perhaps there are lessons to be learned from this form of half day training.

Between 1999 and 2000 the Borough was awarded European Social Funding - Objective 4 (ESF) to help employees in small and medium sized hotel and catering businesses (Subject Matter Experts (SMEs)). The ability to offer low cost high quality training attracted considerably more candidates than in previous years. In 2001 the Council was again awarded ESF - Objective 3 money. The purpose of the funding is to help employees in SMEs with improving skills. Some of the money was also used to help teach potential food hygiene trainers (who speak English as a second language) to deliver food hygiene courses for ESOL candidates.

Discussion with other training organisations, and representatives from the Hospitality Industry, has shown similarities. Managers in 358 of the 1999 survey sample had attended foundation level training compared to 70 who had attended intermediate level training. The London-wide availability of suitably qualified trainers to run basic and intermediate level courses in the languages identified in the 1999 survey is minimal if not non-existent. It penalises non-English speaking students and their employers. Intermediate level examination candidates have shown an increase in failure rates. Feedback from managers and candidates has indicated that the course materials and examination papers were not available in their own languages, nor were they entirely relevant to improving food hygiene in their premises. In addition, some of the questions could not be translated easily. Candidates are reported as having difficulty turning the theory into practice. The external examiners' reports back up these comments. Most commonly reported back to The Directorate of Environmental Health is that the level of written English by certain candidates is not sufficient to pass the examinations.

In June 2001, the Evening Standard reported that 50-80% of catering staff work in London for a year or two to improve their English (Evening Standard, 2001). The Caterer and Hotelkeeper magazine reported that the skills shortage in London was so bad that staff are being recruited from Malaysia and Serbia (Caterer and Hotelkeeper, 2001). As a National Training Organisation, The Hospitality Training Foundation (HtF) undertook research in 1998 to update its original high profile report, *Training who needs it?* which was undertaken in 1995 (HtF, 1998). The survey suggested that restaurant sector provided the least training. The reasons why training was not undertaken included high staff turnover, staff shortages, no employees and a lack of time.

The HtF has anecdotal evidence to suggest that student numbers on all hospitality courses are falling. The focus group was asked to discuss this evidence. Government, accredited examination bodies and attitudes of managers who view overseas food handlers as a source of "cheap labour" concerned all in the group about the lack of intervention to help ESOL food handlers. Accredited examination bodies were contacted for lists of registered trainers who could run food hygiene and health and safety courses in other languages. The advice given was unhelpful. This ranged from the nearest Italian trainer based in Milan, to suggested use of interpreters during training in a room full of other candidates! Registered trainers could run food hygiene courses in Hindi, Gujarati, Bengali, and Punjabi. In the centre of a major conurbation, such as London, there is an acute shortage of suitably qualified trainers who can run the courses in languages for food handlers who come from places other than the sub-continent.

In foundation and intermediate level papers examination questions are not geared towards family or small businesses where supervisors do not exist. There is also the use of the word "hazard" instead of food safety management, and emphasis on design and construction questions. These last two subjects are ones which many candidates know they will have no ability to improve on return to their employers' places of work. Examination questions stress the powers of enforcement officers – rather than emphasising the advice officers can give to businesses. A further difficulty arises with translation, for example, "elderly", "gravy" and "spore" where in some languages there are no direct translations.

The Catering Industry Guide gives unhelpful advice to managers who need to train ESOL food hygiene candidates. It suggests that special arrangements may have to be made for problems of foreign language. There is no further advice about how to make these special arrangements.

Central Government, enforcement agencies, examination bodies, and trainers can no longer continue to expect commercial and institutional food hygiene standards to improve if language barriers cannot be broken down, and managers do not receive the food hygiene training they require. Nor can they expect trainers to fill the gaps for them if the help and resources are not available.

A challenge for the 21st century

In 1999, London employed 5.8% of the UK's hospitality industry workforce (Labour Force Survey, 1999). In July 1999, London had the highest percentage of vacancies (14%) compared to any other region in the UK. The hospitality industry is seen as unglamorous, with long hours and poor pay. More than half of all males in non-manual hospitality industry jobs earned less than £350 per week. These posts within the industry may suit seasonal workers, students, or traveller populations (HtF, 2000).

Hotels and restaurants account for almost 6.1% of employment in London. The number of jobs has grown by 25% (42,500) between 1991 and 1997 (DTZ Pieda Consulting, 1999). Employment in this sector is expected to grow. Cambridge Econometrics forecast growth of 7% (17,000 jobs) to 2010. These posts will consist of part-time and temporary and flexible working patterns (DTZ Pieda Consulting, 1999). It is estimated that the UK's hospitality industry will need to fill 300,000 new jobs before 2009 (Caterer and Hotelkeeper, 2001). One of the key skill requirements for this group will be food hygiene training. However, it is highly likely, that the posts will be filled by considerably more ESOL employees than in recent years, the greater percentage coming from Eastern Europe.

The challenge for this century is to provide food hygiene training for an ever growing number of food handlers who are expected to take up the increasing number of new posts no matter what their level of English. This will fit in with the Government's Adult Learning Strategy, Best Value, Better Government, Equal Opportunities and Social Inclusion policies. As part of planning to meet this challenge the Borough will continue to seek ways to reduce social exclusion, and to make its food hygiene courses available to all. This cannot be done in isolation. Networking with enforcement, educational, business agencies and the hospitality industry will be vital. A co-ordinated approach to resolving the problem of food hygiene training which will benefit *all* food handlers and their managers alike will need careful planning.

The media

Learning may be via the media. For ESOL candidates listening to local radios stations or television channels may prove a useful training tool. In addition use of language and ethnic newspapers are another source which is readily accessible to food business employees. Audio tapes can be used by individuals or groups. Food hygiene messages need to be translated into a range of languages. The use of the text channels on national television (Oracle, Ceefax, etc.) provides a visual source, as does the Open University on BBC2. Unfortunately, the current range of cookery programmes on UK television which are aimed at a domestic audience do little to promote good food hygiene practice. Cable and satellite television may, after careful planning, be utilised to help individuals. A learning medium, which is a growth industry and becoming accessible to increasing numbers of individuals, is information technology.

A way forward

To gain a wider picture of the concerns of organisations and businesses affected by training requirements, and the problems ESOL candidates appear to face with foundation and intermediate level food hygiene examination questions, a series of meetings was organised by the Directorate of Environmental Health. The attendees were from West London Business Link, Portobello Business Service, the Borough's Adult and Community Education, the Learning and Skills Council, trainers from local authority environmental health departments and hospitality industry managers. A way forward was discussed at each of the meetings. The points raised by these groups were then put to the CIEH, the RIPH, the RSPH and the FSA. The meetings took place between July and October 2001.

In summary, the groups suggested the following actions should be taken if food hygiene training is to be effective in its aim of improving food safety, is to be available to food handlers who otherwise may feel socially excluded and is to address the problems managers faced with high turnovers of ESOL candidates:

◆   encourage the examination bodies, training organisations and Central Government to increase the number of trainers to run courses in languages other from from English;

◆   encourage food hygiene trainers and other agencies to work with English language trainers. This will help ESOL candidates develop a better understanding of English to pass basic and intermediate level courses;

◆   run a conference to attract national debate on how best to resolve the problem about the lack of food hygiene trainers who can run courses in other languages apart from English;

◆   totally re-vamp the wording of examinations and syllabuses of the basic level courses. The current one day certificate course need to be changed to a half day, with an expiry date on the certificate. Emphasis on personal hygiene and non-technical hazard analysis is required. Food handlers cannot do much about the fabric of a building and do not need to know about signs and symptoms of pathogens in any great detail;

◆   perhaps introduce critical questions which have to be marked correct for the candidate to pass, or raise the pass mark to 80%. Another problem with the current foundation level examinations is that it is possible to pass without any prior knowledge or attendance on a course. The greatest difficulty is for a candidate to demonstrate practical implementation of the theory. How this is to be resolved is still open for discussion;

◆   for foundation and intermediate level examinations change the questions so that they are relevant to the candidates. Questions with photographs or pictures would be helpful. Asking questions about management responsibilities and the help (rather than emphasis on statutory powers) given by EHOs may press home what owners need to do to improve food safety;

◆   produce food hygiene booklets for candidates and businesses plain in English and a wide range of languages. The use of pictures and tables, rather than long paragraphs of jargon are more conducive to learning or applying theory to practice;

◆   do not fail candidates because they do not speak English (well). Their food hygiene practices, when observed in the workplace, may be more than adequate;

◆   promote wider use of computer-based training (CBT) for all candidates to reinforce the proposed half day foundation courses. Planned CBT would be the responsibility of proprietors of food businesses. The advantages of this type of training may include absorption of information over a longer period of time and it does not remove the candidate from the work place for long periods of time;

◆   change the current legislation to require the owner of a food premises to undergo at least intermediate level training. Produce non-technical syllabuses, examination questions and materials in other languages apart from English, which are relevant to everyday catering operations. Food handlers should attend a half day examined food hygiene course and the onus of further training placed upon the managers of premises; and

♦ through the FSA set up a Food Safety Education Alliance. Members of the alliance would be trainers from a range of public and private sectors, plus any examination body or government agency which has an interest in food safety training. The Food and Drugs Administration in the USA funds the Food Safety Training and Education Alliance. Free membership gives members access to a range of relevant websites, training material production news, and considerable information about how to train non-English-speaking food handlers.

The group consisting of businesses advisors and adult education service providers suggested that funding initiatives such as European Social Funding were made more widely available to help with the cost of training potential trainers. Also closer links could be made with colleges to organise special courses for ESOL candidates.

Managers from the hospitality industry who attended the meetings were not aware of the shortage of trainers to run the courses in other languages. It was suggested that their own industry could do more to seek out potential trainers to help themselves. The examinations at basic and intermediate level were in need of change. Words could not always be easily translated, terminology such as "Hazard Analysis" is easily misunderstood, the questions in the papers are not a fair representation of everyday catering situations. More pictures would help. Training sessions for managers may be useful if local authorities were to organise food safety forums. This would allow for two-way feedback on subjects concerning food safety management, training, addressing language barriers, and compliance with food safety law.

Representatives from Central London local authority environmental health departments met to discuss their concerns about the training on offer, the lack of adequate explanation about training requirements in the Industry Guides, and the concern about the relevance of some examination questions to food handlers dealing with different menus (for example, vegetarian, pizza, coffee shop menus). Language barriers were encountered on courses, and many candidates from ethnic minority backgrounds had literacy difficulties. Syllabuses and the examination questions did not reflect the legislation. Both need complete overhauls. For example, questions testing knowledge of candidates about storage of cold food at room temperature must take into account the four hour rule (detailed in the Food Safety (Temperature Control) Regulations 1995) which permits cold food to be prepared, displayed and sold at room temperature within four hours. The safety of defrosting a chicken at room temperature for 12 hours compared to using a refrigerator to prevent the growth of spoilage organisms is not taken into account in certain examination questions. Questions at foundation and intermediate level need to reflect the advantages businesses can gain from speaking to their local authority environmental health departments. Half day courses for all food handlers culminating in a short tick test with critical questions relating to time and temperature control might be a more suitable form of training than the current foundation courses on offer. Managers should undergo some training to help them manage food safety rather than just learn about food hygiene theory to help them pass an examination. The local authority officers decided it would be beneficial for them to meet quarterly or six-monthly to discuss current training issues. This will enable representation to be made to the appropriate agencies or organisations, to express views and concerns.

Issues discussed at the meetings were put to the accredited examination bodies and the Food Standards Agency. There was general interest in this whole area. Questions were raised such as: "Are we training or testing?", "Are there clear distinctions between training and qualifications?", and "Training, testing, or implementation – which is the most important?". Some of the points provided discussion and generated ideas for long-term changes. However, all agreed some training was better than no training. The issue of language trainers and difficulties some food handlers faced with attending courses was accepted. It was considered important to remember why training took place – namely to improve standards. The content and style of course delivery was important. There was a view that any new course should be delivered in English first. Once any creases had been ironed out then the course could be adapted to meet other ethnic needs. Race relations and discrimination legislation may influence the future of any legally required food hygiene training. This area is to be explored. Mandatory training was for the moment ruled out. Any change will have to be carefully considered.

The Borough is to continue to find ways forward to help ESOL food handlers. These include networking with the Hospitality Training Foundation, the Learning and Skills Council, West London Business Link, Portobello Business Centre, accredited examination bodies, the Food Standards Agency, other local authorities, NHS Primary Care Groups, adult education providers, employment agencies, charitable and voluntary organisations, community and welfare groups and trade associations. It is committed to improving skills and education standards, maximising European funding, assisting local businesses, and seeking new partnerships to improve employability and business stability.

Rennie said that "although no training programme is complete without an evaluation of its effectiveness, there are relatively few reported evaluations of the effectiveness of food hygiene education in the UK. Those which have been identified do not make the case convincingly for food hygiene education in its current form" (Rennie,1994). To date there are still no evaluations which determine the effectiveness of food hygiene courses. However, the Food Standards Agency appears to be taking a small step in the right direction with its forthcoming Catering Campaign.

Maybe it is time for the accredited examination bodies, along with the FSA, NHS Primary Health Care Trusts, and the Hospitality Industry to review the few evaluations which Rennie identified, and to open-mindedly review the current food hygiene training strategy for the UK?

Other barriers

Finally, trainers may well wish to consider other barriers created by poor communication:

♦ Messages: These may become contradictory when too many people are involved in the communication process. Trainers running a course may say one thing, the enforcement officer may say another, and the owner of a business may interpret the advice from the former and the instruction from the latter in his/her own way – after seeking the opinion from colleagues, family and others.

♦ Emphasis by the trainer: the food handlers on the training programme may want to put into practice the key points emphasised by the trainer, but their manager has other commitments and priorities, or, for example, does not have much time for staff development.

- ◆ Forgetfulness and interpretation: language and memory retention, different levels of English, or mother tongue as a written, or spoken language, ability to cope with technical words or subjects, etc.

- ◆ Cultural and social gaps: ethnicity, religious beliefs, social background, economic values, gender values and interests will need to be considered.

- ◆ Limited uptake and feed back: trainers may try their best at training and getting to know their target audience. However, as the saying goes "you can lead a horse to water, but you can't make it drink". Mental health issues, impaired health, stress, pre-occupation, distractions, negative beliefs, and sickness may all present reasons for trainees putting up barriers to being trained.

- ◆ Suspicion: the trainees and their employers may distrust the trainer, the organisation they represent, resent the presence of a stranger in their premises, or may have had experience of bad training in the past.

In addition to the above, age should not be overlooked. "Ageism", or age discrimination is shortly to be made illegal by the EU. It is worth considering that in the UK:
- ◆ in 2002 half of the electorate and a half of the workforce were over the age of 45;
- ◆ by year 2020 the population over the age of 45 will rise significantly;
- ◆ up to 2020 the population under the age of 45 will reduce with equal significance; and
- ◆ nearly a third of over 45s are without work (some 2.8 millions).

Managers should not discriminate over age. In addition, for the over 45s who are currently unemployed or seeking a move into a food handling post, attending a course and undergoing training will increase their opportunities for employment. For existing food handlers, managers should certainly not deprive anyone over 45 years old the chance to further themselves by attending courses and receiving suitable food hygiene training and/or instruction.

Conclusion

Ralph Waldo Emerson (1803 to 1882) wrote: "Is it bad to be misunderstood? Pythagoras was misunderstood, and Socrates, and Jesus, and Luther, and Copernicus, and Galileo, and Newton, and every pure and wise spirit that ever took flesh. To be great is to be misunderstood." The answer to the question in the quotation must be "yes". Food hygiene trainers have a moral obligation to ensure that all their target audiences understand them and are able to turn theory into practice. Trainers must not discriminate against those who are faced with barriers to overcome. The skilled trainer will remove those barriers and make training accessible to all. Ralph Waldo Emerson also wrote: "If a man writes a better book, preaches a better sermon, or makes a better mouse trap than his neighbour, tho' he build his house in the woods, the world will make a path to his door." It is from this point that trainers must begin.

A radical co-ordinated re-think and shake up of foundation and intermediate level food hygiene courses and examinations are required if ESOL food handlers, and ultimately their customers, are to benefit from improved practical implementation of food hygiene matters commensurate with their work activities. A clearer explanation of training requirements and recommendations is required in the Industry Guides with greater emphasis on competency.

Central Government, the Sector Skills Council (formerly the National Training Organisation), the hospitality industry, business advisory agencies, and trainers will have to work together with a common goal. That goal is to help food handlers, whatever their language, receive appropriate accessible theoretical training which can be turned in to practice. This must done with input from local authorities, the accredited examination bodies and adult education or training providers.

To sum up, the barriers to effective food hygiene training are basic skills (numeracy and literacy) and the use of English as a second language, ageism, and the basic use of keyboard skills.

Further reading

♦ Ewles, L and Simnett, I (1992) *Promoting Health: A practical guide.* London: Scutari Press;
♦ Gittins, R (1998) *An Introduction to Literacy Skills.* London: The Basic Skills Agency; and
♦ Shackman, J (1987) *The Right to be understood – a handbook on working with employing and training community interpreters.* Cambridge: National Extension College

6 Training Skills

"Better to keep your mouth shut and appear stupid than to open it and remove all doubt." (Mark Twain 1835-1910)

A starting point

"I tell them what I will tell them. I tell them what I told them I would tell them. Then, I tell them what I told them I would tell them!"

An experienced instructor in 1978 relayed the above quotation to the author, during his first introduction to training at the Royal Army Medical Corps School of Army Health in Hampshire. Like every instructor or trainer the style of delivery changes according to the individual needs of both the trainees and the message which has to be passed on. Training now compared to twenty years ago has moved away from straightforward "telling" to active participation and involvement by the trainees.

Adopting the maxims "if it can go wrong, it will", and "be prepared for the worst" will give the novice trainer some idea of the monumental but rewarding task they are to take on. This task is of course helping to feed trainees' knowledge and provide them with understanding, and the ability to be able to demonstrate that they can put into practice what they have been taught.

In this chapter the reader will gain an insight into the fundamental necessities of basic training skills. The idea is to help those who have never trained before to put some structure to their presentation.

The reader is encouraged to:
- read some of the titles suggested in the further reading;
- practise their style of delivery before confronting the candidates;
- talk to other trainers about delivery techniques; and
- experiment using different visual materials or aids.

In this chapter the reader will learn about the basics of:
- how people learn;
- setting learning outcomes;
- planning training sessions;
- facilitating learning;
- training groups; and
- organising a course.

How people learn

The trainer is faced with the responsibility of promoting the desire to learn amongst trainees and motivating them enough to implement what they have learnt. The trainer needs to arouse interest in subject matter – some education psychologists say that the first fifteen seconds of any training session are vital – others say that the maximum attention span for a trainee is 17 minutes. So what helps or hinders learning?

Think of two occasions when you have been on the receiving end of training, such as when you were a student in a class, or in the audience listening to a talk, or if you have been taught on a one-to-one basis. The factors that would have helped or hindered your learning would have been the presentation, the trainer, and the environment. The table below illustrates typical reactions.

	PRESENTATION	TRAINER	ENVIRONMENT
GOOD	Lively	Friendly	Comfortable
	Humourous	Interesting	Well lit
	Visual	Enthusiastic	Ventilated
	Informative	Fair	Spacious
BAD	Too long	Unfriendly	Hot
	Irrelevant	Boring	Cold
	Too fast	Unclear	Poor seating
	Muddled	Mannerisms	Distractions

So, when do food handlers need training? Examples of occasions include:
- before starting a new job;
- continuously;
- when determined by a training needs assessment;
- identified when HACCP is implemented, for example, monitoring techniques;
- new menus, or equipment;
- changes in legislation;
- the service of notices under the provisions of Food Safety Act 1990; and
- when something has gone wrong or a customer complaint.

So then, how do people learn? The best way is by letting the trainees become involved and being able to demonstrate that they can put into practice what they have been taught. Make the trainees feel that they are a part of the training process and not an end product. Competency and behavioural changes are key in the improvement of food hygiene practice – rather than just passing a food hygiene certificated examination. A range of different learning situations are now available to trainees:
- one-to-one with a mentor;
- in a classroom setting;
- using training posters;
- self-study by reading books and information;
- e-learning and using CBT; and
- team or brigade projects.

Generally it is thought that trainees remember:
- 10% of what they read;

- 20% of what they hear;
- 30% of what they see;
- 50% of what they hear and see;
- 70% of what they say; and
- 90% of what they say as they do a task.

Learning implies some changes in behaviour brought about by our experience of the environment. Clinical and experimental psychologists have established that the way our five senses contribute to learning are as follows:

- Seeing   80%
- Hearing   14%
- Touching   2%
- Tasting   2%
- Smell   2%

Psychologists generally agree that there is about 30% more comprehension and 50% more retention when multi-sensory channels of communication are used.

How can an individual influence the learning process? A whole range of issues need to be considered, such as:

Culture	Religion	Written and learning ability	Attentiveness	Age and health
Attitude	Previous experience	Co-operation	Not jumping ahead	Self perception

A group can influence the learning process too, for example, by:

Speaking all at once	Following the herd	Peer pressure	Electing a spokesperson	Singling out weak participants
Asking irrelevant questions	Speaking down the trainer	Talking	Co-operating with the trainer	Helping other trainees

What are the qualities of a good trainer? As this is a book about food hygiene training, perhaps the following recipe instructions will suffice:

"Take an exceptional amount of *enthusiasm* and mix it with *great industry in preparation*. To this mixture add sufficient sense of purpose to make it *clear of objective*. Simmer gently, stirring in a good measure of *knowledge* and *experience*. Add essence of *imagination* to ensure a spectacular presentation. Garnish with a *pleasant manner* to taste. Knead the mixture until it acquires a *fair, firm* and *friendly attitude*, and set it out to *practice…*"

Design of training and development is concerned with the identification of:

- the required outcome and benefits;
- methods and approaches to training;
- the range of employees, target groups and individuals;
- the programming and scheduling; and

♦ communicating the availability and range of programmes to employers/ees and the creation of systems which help the activity take place.

The design of the course or programme will have to include content, method, timing, administration, registration etc. For trainers to deliver the Foundation Certificate in Food Hygiene courses they must be registered with one of the awarding bodies. Also they must have a recognised training skills qualification. During the 1970s and 1980s, the Hotel and Catering Industry Training Board (now HtF) developed a range of training skills courses. HM Forces developed their Methods of Instruction courses. NVQs in training and development now exist with specific units (D32-36) concerned with the design, delivery and evaluation of training.

Learning outcomes

What is meant by "learning outcomes"? Possibly: The knowledge gained by study or receiving training. Remember that learning is a voluntary process. If this is the case how can a trainer get trainees to want to learn and assimilate the knowledge that is going to be passed on to them? Perhaps some of the ways to achieve learning and its expected or anticipated outcomes are:

♦ creating an interest;
♦ developing an interest; and
♦ maintaining the desire to learn.

The interest will be developed with participation, an active use of all the senses, and good use of eye contact to make all the trainees feel part of the learning process. Trainers should ask themselves: "Is what I teach what I want to teach or what my trainees want to learn? Am I attempting too much in too short a space of time? Will the trainees be able to put into practice what I plan to teach them?"

Creating an interest…
BEFORE the training session create an interest:

♦ handout a programme to inform and interest the trainees; and
♦ advertise with posters.

DURING the introduction develop an interest:

♦ clearly state the training objective.

"What I intend to do is to …"	teach you	about		S so that	State…
	show you			U at the	List…
"My objective is to…"	explain to you	the		B end of	Identify…
				J this lesson	Solve…
	prove to you			E you will	Calculate…
"I am going to…"	illustrate for you			C be able	Recognise…
				T to…	Etc…

♦ tell the trainees the reason why the subject matter is important (e.g. "…this may help you to understand how to use a cleaning schedule effectively.")
♦ provide a personal incentive (e.g. "…this may stop you or your family from falling ill.")

MAINTAIN the desire to learn by keeping the group/class/or individual interested in the lesson:

- be enthusiastic – it can be contagious;
- get trainees involved from the beginning;
- take maximum advantage of senses;
- be as realistic as is practicable (use experiences without any exaggeration);
- keep training at the correct level for the group;
- seek a variety of training techniques;
- avoid distractions and mannerisms; and
- develop good questioning techniques.

Aims and objectives

From the very beginning of the training session the trainer must be clear about aims and objectives. If the session is about cleaning food equipment do not stray on to the subject of personal hygiene or spore formation unless absolutely relevant to the point of the intended session subject.

An *aim* states the intention of what the training is setting out to achieve, for example:

- to meet the needs of the individual;
- to meet the needs of the company;
- to comply with a specific legal requirement; and
- to increase knowledge in a specific area of food hygiene.

An *objective* sets out the required learning outcomes. Training objectives are clear and unambiguous statements of exactly what the trainees have to do at the end of the training sessions. In theory they eliminate the risks of under- and over-training by describing exactly what has to be learnt. Formulation of objectives tell:

- the employer what the employee(s) will learn;
- the employee(s) what has to be learnt;
- the trainer what s/he has to teach; and
- the examiner or assessor what s/he has to test or assess.

Training objectives provide the yardstick against which a trainer can assess the efficiency and effectiveness of his/her training. Objectives are measurable, whereas aims are not. Training objectives have three components:

- performance;
- conditions; and
- standards.

Performance states what trainees will have to do at the end of the training session. For example:

Providing an objective such as "to improve morale" would be misleading. It is an aim. To use it as an objective it is unclear, not measurable and unlikely to have the desired effect.

An example, commonly used by awarding bodies could be "Food poisoning: The expected outcome is that the student knows the symptoms and main causes of food poisoning and is able to:

- explain what is meant by the terms food hygiene, food poisoning, and contamination;
- describe the symptoms of food poisoning; and
- state the causes of food poisoning."

PERFORMANCE	CONDITIONS	STANDARDS
Test the temperature of hot meat pie	Given: ♦ freshly baked meat pie; ♦ probe thermometer; ♦ record chart; and ♦ disinfecting wipes.	♦ washes hands before handling food and probe; ♦ disinfects the probe; ♦ probes the pie; ♦ records the temperature; ♦ informs supervisor of results; and ♦ disinfects the probe before putting away.

At the end of any training session confirmation is required that the objective has been achieved. This ensures that one step in the process is completed before another one is attempted. Confirmation allows trainees to clear up any doubts which they may have had and to develop a sense of achievement. This will help them to maintain an interest in the topic the trainer is trying to get across.

Audio Visual Aids (AVAs)

There are many different types of AVAs. Further information is given in the chapter called "Resources to Use". They enhance a training session and can be used (with practice) very effectively to reinforce a teaching point or to clear up any difficulties. The list below shows just a few of the materials trainers use:

Flip chart	Dry Board	Blanket boards	Chalk board	Magnetic boards
Slide projector	PowerPoint	Tape recorder	Television	Video recorder/player
Personal or laptop computers	Overhead projector	Games	Leaflets/booklets	Posters/charts
Photographs	Specimens	Equipment	Fake or real food	Documents/manuals

Consider the main function of AVAs. It is to assist the understanding of the trainee – not as a substitute for the trainer. A variety of realistic aids will stimulate the trainee and help with learning. The desire to learn will be maintained. AVAs are also used as prompts by trainers. However there are positive and negative values associated with choice of AVAs. These include:

POSITIVE		NEGATIVE	
Increase motivation Arouse interest		Demotivating Waffling	

POSITIVE		NEGATIVE	
Encourage interest Provoke discussion To present key facts		Poor quality Distracting Too much information	

When selecting an AVA the trainer must ensure it is :

♦ **Necessary:** An AVA should only be used if it is required to make training easier to understand.

♦ **Most suitable:** The most easily available aid is not necessarily the most suitable for the purpose. The trainer must be imaginative.

♦ **Simple:** As the purpose of the AVA is to simplify training it follows that the AVA should be as brief as possible and only contain the essentials. An AVA must not confuse the issue by the inclusion of unnecessary detail.

♦ **Large enough:** An AVA must be large enough (or loud enough) for the individual or the group to see (or hear) clearly and comfortably.

♦ **Interesting:** It is desirable to produce the most interesting aids for the purpose. Colour, layout, humour and realism will add interest. Be careful of suitability, necessity, and how others may perceive the humour (it may be offensive or not understood).

Common faults include putting too much detail on an acetate, out-of-focus projectors, poor tracking on a video tape and illegible flipchart notes.

Effective use of AVAs will include:

♦ **Rehearsal:** Make sure you are well versed in the use of the AVA before showing the trainees.

♦ **Display:** Keep the AVA out of sight, or in a position where, until required, it will not cause distraction.

♦ **Describe:** If using an AVA to back up training, tell trainees what they are looking at or listening to.

♦ **Teach:** An AVA without explanation is of no value to the trainees or trainers.

♦ **Dispose:** Once an AVA has been used, remove it from sight or to a place where it will not cause distraction. Re-use it to confirm salient teaching points.

Training groups

This section is concerned with recognising the characteristics of groups and their development and the place of the individual trainee in any group. There is a need to develop the skills of encouragement and participation, and the ability to recognise traits to be avoided.

Typical characteristics of groups and of individuals include:

♦ knowing why they are to be trained;

♦ previous experience;

♦ previous qualifications;

♦ asking for introductions;

♦ discussing skills/weaknesses with managers/supervisors; and

♦ prior knowledge of religious, cultural and language factors which may influence delivery of training.

Some groups will be extroverted, introverted or a mixture of the two. It is important not to pick on one individual or to show favouritism. Try to treat all trainees with equality and respect. Forward planning and information about your trainees may help with preparing for the delivery of a session. Consider which subject matter you will have to spend more time on or the way in which the message is to be put across. Where feasible offer extra training or one-to-one on-site practical training. Use plain English and simple diagrams. Consider trainees who do not speak English as a first language, have special needs, or who have learning difficulties.

Mixed courses with managers, supervisors and subordinates do not always work. The latter may be reluctant to contribute, just as the former may dominate a session.

Encourage individuals to share examples (where relevant) related to their places of work. If the course ends in an examination or test explain to the individuals exactly what they can expect. Above all make sure that the questions are relevant to an individual's job (if they are not expected to be multi-skilled). For example: do not talk about shepherd's pie production to food handlers who just produce sausages, or cook-chill to silver service staff.

A good trainer will give credit or praise where it is due, encourage individual participation, get the trainees to move around the room and work in different groups, and will be firm, fair and polite. Key training and teaching principles include:

1. **Work from the known to unknown**
    Start with something the trainees know about. This will help the trainer establish how much is already known.

2. **Aim for maximum involvement**
    Passive learning is not enjoyable! Get to know the trainees and get them involved from the start. Breaking down barriers can help remove nerves from the trainees and trainers too.

3. **Vary methods of teaching**
    Using a variety of AVAs and changing the training methods will give the trainer a break, trainees variety and a chance to participate, maintain concentration, and involve all the senses.

4. **Ensure relevance**
    Recommendations, examples, statistics, case studies, codes of practice must all be relevant to the subject which is being taught.

5. **Identify realistic goals and objectives**
    Do not try to teach too much. If an answer to a question from a trainee is not known be honest and find out later. Waffle can lead to long-winded discussions which are difficult to end.

6. **Organise materials**
    Whatever the choice of materials, they must be relevant, understandable to all the trainees, training needs analysis and up-to-date.

7. **Carry out a training needs analysis and post training evaluation**
    Training needs analysis (TNA) will, for example, help the business identify what is required to modify its food safety culture. It will indicate what groups of employees need to do to improve their performance. Finally, at an individual employee level it

will identify present attitude, knowledge and ability to do their job satisfactorily. This will help with planning the type of training required to move the employee up an ability level. Evaluations will help the trainer to identify what has to be taught, how the training went, and what needs to be changed in the future to effect better standards of food safety.

8.   **Avoid traits and mannerisms**
Fidgets, mannerisms, repetition, favouritism, pacing about the room, speaking quietly/loudly/fast/slowly etc. can be very distracting for the trainees.

Facilitating learning
This section is concerned with:
- the use of questions to teach or to test;
- the utilisation of groups and syndicates to encourage interactive learning; and
- the appropriate use of learning support facilities.

The use of questions to teach or to test
Questioning is a technique which must be understood by trainers. This technique, coupled with a comprehensive knowledge of the subject, will enable trainees to remain attentive, alert, and active. The purpose of asking questions is threefold:
- to test by checking the knowledge of a group or an individual;
- to teach by asking the group or individual to assess learning; and
- to create activity by keeping the group or individual alert.

Readers may be able to remember a time when a teacher or trainer suddenly asked them a question without warning. How did they feel? Embarrassed, uncomfortable, etc?

When training a group it is important to aim the question at the whole group. Pose the question, pause to let the trainees think about their answers, then nominate someone to give an answer. Do make sure that the questions are clear, unambiguous and relevant to the aims and objectives. Never test trainees' powers of expression or language ability.

Let the trainees ask questions. But beware! Questions from trainees can fall into three groups – relevant, irrelevant and those to which the trainer does not know the answer. Skilful and sympathetic handling by the trainer of questions from the group or individual saves valuable time, reduces irrelevancy and maintains interest.

Encouraging interactive learning
There are specific training techniques to encourage interactive learning. A straight forward lecture may be economical in terms of the lecturer's time but it does not allow for group participation, motivation or an assessment of whether the message has been understood.

Interactive learning techniques include:

♦ Syndicate methods	♦ Lecturettes	♦ Discussion groups
♦ Exercises	♦ Competitions	♦ Quizzes
♦ Role play	♦ Assignments	♦ Skills training
♦ Informal training	♦ Computer based training	♦ Wordsearches.

Training conditions

The trainer, having considered the subject matter, must be able to define exactly what the trainee should be able to do and under what conditions s/he will be able to do it. The following must be taken into consideration:

- ◆ Time: How long the period is, etc.
- ◆ Class: How many in the group, their aptitude, prior knowledge, etc.
- ◆ Subject matter: What is to be taught, how and in what order.
- ◆ Assessment: Written or practical assessments, multiple choice or oral examinations

Methods of presentation, AVAs, administration, conditions of learning environment, names of trainees and a logical plan are necessary. In addition, special needs, learning difficulties and language have to be taken into account.

KNOWLEDGE SESSION

A knowledge or facts session has a beginning, middle and end. No training will succeed without a plan. Thorough planning, preparation and practice will contribute to the performances of not only the trainer but also the trainees.

Timing and rehearsal

A full rehearsal of the whole session, including use of AVAs, is necessary. This avoids embarrassment on the part of the trainer, and restlessness on the part of the trainee(s). A 10 to 15 minute session will consist of: beginning (2-3 minutes), middle (6-8 minutes), end (3-5 minutes). A 40 minute session will consist of: beginning (5-10 minutes), middle (20-25 minutes), end (5-10 minutes).

Beginning:

Preliminaries, for example:

- ◆ checking for distractions;
- ◆ checking trainees' names; and
- ◆ safety instructions.

Equipment checks should be made before trainees are in place to see if everything works. Once the trainees are in place ask them if they can see the equipment and whatever it is that is being projected.

Revision - The main reason for revision is to ensure that the candidates have the necessary knowledge to progress. It also provides a link with previous training and can switch the trainee's mind to the subject under study.

Training objectives - Reasons why s/he needs to know about a particular subject (and where relevant include a personal incentive).

Middle:

This part is where the training is presented. Depending upon the group there should be no more than 3 or 4 teaching points.

End:

Final confirmation - To assess that training has been assimilated and the objectives achieved.

Packing-up – This is done before or after the summary. Put visual materials away.

Summary - To emphasise salient points.

Look forward - The opportunity should be taken to arouse interest if the class or group is to attend any future training session.

SKILLS LESSON

The planning of skills training differs from that of a knowledge lesson in the middle part only. It has four easily recognisable phases in each stage of the middle that are designed to give the trainees the maximum amount of practical work. Consider where and when skills training to improve food safety standards would be necessary. For instance: handwashing, cleaning, and using a probe thermometer. It is difficult to allocate timings for each phase of a skills lesson. Approximately 70% of the time should be given over to implementation and practice (the middle stage).

♦ **Explanation** – this entails a clear and simple description of the equipment and a concise explanation of the operation.

♦ **Demonstration** – the trainer demonstrates the operation at normal operating speed, to show the trainee the standard s/he is expected to achieve. The trainer repeats the process at a slower speed, clearly showing each progressive stage in the complete operation.

♦ **Implementation** – The trainee(s) start(s) to perform the operation under the control of the trainer. Each stage of the operation is checked by the trainer, in order to prevent the trainees from developing faults or bad habits when learning to perform the skill(s) required.

♦ **Practice** – In this phase, the trainer gives the trainee opportunities to practise the skills s/he has learnt. The trainer must adopt an imaginative approach to this phase (e.g. exercise the candidate in different situations at different speeds with improved dexterity) until all the trainees are able to perform the standards set out in the training objectives for that lesson.

To conclude a skills lesson, the end of the training will provide the trainees with an opportunity to ask questions and clear up any doubts they may have. The trainer must remember to ask questions and confirm understanding throughout each phase. The more time the trainee has to practise the better chance s/he has of passing a practical assessment or assignment.

ORGANISING A COURSE

Non-trainers and managers that rely on experienced trainers to run courses often fail to appreciate how much work goes into organising courses. Unlike John Buchan's Thirty Nine Steps there are often as many as 60 to 90 steps involved. The trainer has to make plans long before facing the candidates and long after the course has been delivered. This section endeavours to group some of the key steps necessary to ensure the successful organisation of a course.

Organising a successful course or training programme involves:
♦ selecting a venue;
♦ determining course size;
♦ costing a course;
♦ administration and security;
♦ preparing a programme;
♦ marketing and taking bookings;
♦ preparing course notes and training cards;
♦ deciding on audio visual aids and resources;
♦ running a course; and
♦ evaluation.

Preparing a programme

The trainer must decide on the content and teaching or learning strategy. This will include the syllabus and scheme of work:

♦ **Syllabus:** Defined as the outline of a course of study or the list of subjects studied in the course. Examination bodies such as CIEH, RIPH, RSPH, REHIS, and SOFHT already have syllabuses that contain the information that candidates must know in order for them to be entered for and pass the examinations. Multi-skilled food handlers will need a more general syllabus. However, not every syllabus is suitable for food handlers who have specific jobs within their business.

♦ **Scheme of Work:** Any scheme of work should organise the topics of the syllabus so that they are presented in a way that assists learning by means of logical progression. This means: simple to complex; familiar to unfamiliar; and practical to theoretical (or vice versa). Foundation food hygiene certificate courses are generally organised as follows:
  ♦ introduction to and importance of food hygiene;
  ♦ causes of food poisoning;
  ♦ basic microbiology;
  ♦ cross-contamination;
  ♦ food preservation and storage;
  ♦ personal hygiene;
  ♦ cleaning and disinfection;
  ♦ design and layout of premises;
  ♦ equipment design;
  ♦ pest control; and
  ♦ legislation.

The topics listed above may be grouped or even replaced by words such as hazard analysis; and food safety management.

The scheme of work will show the duration of a topic or particular course, for example, session one on Friday in the morning, and session two ten days later in the afternoon. Or, Friday at midnight (yes! food handlers need training at night if they are on shift and on-site training is required), or on a Saturday at 11pm.

Lesson plans are discussed later in this chapter.

Bookings and room choice

The trainer has arranged the course programme, got the trainees to turn up on time at the appointed venue and then it comes to the crunch – the trainer realises that the room booking has not been confirmed, the exam papers have been forgotten, there is nowhere to plug in the computer for a PowerPoint display, or something equally bad. The trainees may even have difficulty in hearing you if steam cleaning is being carried out or there is a cellar delivery, etc. You may have a booked room but failed to check that it was not located next to a dual carriageway, or in main corridor of a restaurant. Whatever bookings are made, a dress rehearsal is vital. Consider the following:

♦ is the location appropriate?
♦ what is the seating like?
♦ are there sufficient tables?
♦ is there sufficient room for practical training?
♦ will glare affect computer based training?
♦ is the venue accessible?
♦ security and fire evacuation?
♦ invoicing?
♦ refreshments and welfare facilities?

AVAs and resources

These have been discussed in more depth elsewhere in this book. However, it can do no harm to remind the reader that AVAs and resources must be suitable for the task in hand, and must be designed to ensure that the trainees will actually learn from them. Check that any information given to the trainees is up-to-date, and if it is in print consider language and special needs.

General administration, safety and security

It is surprising how many managers of food businesses ask an external trainer to run training sessions on site whether it is at the workplace or somewhere like a private dining room for a seated course. Once the trainer is on site the manager immediately forgets their obligations under Section 3 of the Health & Safety at Work Act 1974, namely not considering the health, safety and welfare of the visiting trainer. Equally, the trainer has obligations under the Act as well to ensure that their activities do not affect their own, their trainees', or anybody's health and safety in that premises.

Always give general consideration to who, how and when to inform about venues, refreshments, messages, public transport, fire drills, smoking, WCs, examinations and registration. These can take a considerable amount of time to relay to the trainees.

The trainees will also need to know where to go for their training and any reception or security staff in the building will need to be informed. Once the trainees are seated there will be registration and details to give them about security whilst in the venue.

It will be equally necessary to inform any examination body about the course, trainees and date of examination which they are to be entered for. If the trainees have attempted an examination, decide how they will be notified a of success or failure. Some system of recording the results will be necessary.

Course numbers

If the trainer is running a formal course between 8 to 15 candidates are an ideal number. However, there are no hard and fast rules because the type of training will be dependent upon the identified training needs of individuals and groups. The training may be on a one-to-one practical basis using a sanitising agent, or training a manager how to inspect a kitchen. It could also be classroom based for foundation or intermediate food hygiene certificate trainees.

Course notes

Successful delivery by the trainer requires a lesson plan and prompt cards. Alternatively, acetates or PowerPoint presentations can be designed to facilitate prompting.

Costing a course

The syllabus has been organised, course notes rehearsed, trainees identified, and then it comes to the crunch. How much is the whole training project going to cost? The cost per trainee and what is included in the cost need to be identified. Does a training budget exist, or has a profit to be made? Expenditure on materials may be limited but it is surprising how often trainers forget that practical training sessions can take place in a workplace full of props.

The table below will give some idea of what needs to be taken into account. For the purposes of this example the calculations are for a course of ten trainees who are to undertake a one day Foundation Certificate in Food Hygiene. The reader should not rely on the figures given as they are only used for an illustration of a six-hour course.

Registration & Examination fees @ £9.50 per trainee	£95.00
Food Hygiene booklet at £2.00 per copy	£20.00
Trainer's time @ £15 per hour for 10 hours	£150.00
Administration time @ £10 per hour @ 15 minutes per candidate	£25.00
Photocopying (handouts) @ 50p per candidate	£5.00
Coffee and biscuits @ 40 per candidate	£4.00
AVA materials	£10.00
Perishables	£5.00
Agar plates	£6.00
Total:	*£320.00*
10% profit	£32.00
Charge per candidate less VAT	*£35.20*

Other expenses which may need to be taken into account are:
♦ room hire and food;
♦ equipment purchase; and
♦ training packs which may include materials and videos.

Examination bodies usually charge a trainer registration fee. This has been omitted from the calculations above. Figures between organisations and in-house costs will vary.

Planning a training session

This section involves:
- planning a training session from an analysis of specific knowledge or skill required;
- structuring training sessions into introduction, development and checking with each element showing a logical structure; and
- competently delivering a training session.

To be successful, any period of training must be well planned and prepared. This requires time, effort and imagination on behalf of the trainer, trainee and their manager(s). Many factors have to be considered in the planning and preparation, and then placed in a logical order for the presentation.

Evaluation

The syllabuses produced by the CIEH, RSPH, RIPH, REHIS and SOFHT are always useful sources of reference. They make a good starting point when formulating objectives. Be wary, however - these organisations all have different ways of laying out the syllabuses for various certificated examinations. It is vital to consider whether the examination bodies' aims and objectives really meet the aims and objectives of the training required for your business and for your employees. For instance, if they are involved in wholesale doughnut production why train them about café food hygiene?

Consider for the moment, what is understood by the term "to assess attainment of the desired outcomes"? Possibly "evaluation of training" or "confirmation of training". As stated elsewhere in this book, competency is far more important in terms of improving food safety than receiving a certificate. The function of evaluation is to check whether the content stated in the objectives have been achieved. Evaluation can take many forms. Depending upon the nature of the business and activities of the trainees, evaluation may start before any formal training takes place, during training, and once the trainees have returned to their places of work. Typical evaluation methods include:
- direct questioning;
- general questioning;
- feedback from group;
- written test, or computer based tests;
- project-based assignments;
- practical demonstration;
- group work to achieve an end product; and
- observation by management, consultants, peers, or enforcement officers.

Once a course or period of training has been undertaken it will be necessary to carry out some form of evaluation. This will help to assess whether the aims and objectives have been achieved. Evaluation simply means making a judgement about the value of something. It is the process of assessing what has been achieved and how it has been achieved.

The reasons for evaluation are to:
- improve the trainer's performance;
- help others improve their practice;
- justify the use of resources;
- give the trainer job satisfaction;

- identify unexpected outcomes;
- find out what the trainees felt about the course; and
- establish what further training is required.

As previously mentioned, a training needs analysis should be undertaken before the course. This will help identify any need for behavioural changes. Trainees may be given post-course evaluation forms at the end of any training. Employers, too, can be given evaluation forms to provide feedback to help with an assessment of any changes that have occurred since the training took place. Depending upon the type of training that has been undertaken, the trainer may find it useful to carry out a post-course evaluation in the workplace. This will enable an assessment of the trainees' pre- and post-course behavioural changes in attitude.

Points to consider for an evaluation form include:

- name of trainee;
- business details;
- name of trainer;
- training venue;
- date of training;
- name of course/type of training;
- were the aims and objectives met successfully?
- which aspects were particularly useful?
- which aspects were least useful?
- which topics were presented in too much depth?
- which topics required more time?
- administrative, catering and accommodation facilities;
- how did the trainee hear about the course?
- why did the trainee attend?
- what does the trainee hope to achieve after the course?
- what specific aspects of the training are going to be put into practice?
- overall comments about the course or training;
- how could the course be improved? and
- future training requirements.

Proceed with caution! What will the trainer be testing when exposing a trainee to an evaluation form? Trainees may have language, numeracy or literacy difficulties which prevent them from satisfactorily completing the forms. For these reasons, consider whether a tick box style form, numerical scoring or questions which allow for written answers are best.

Some examination bodies provide guidance for the wording of evaluation forms. Trainers may produce their own, or the businesses that have requested the training may insist on using theirs. Whichever style the wording takes be careful about readability and the target audience.

Once the evaluation forms have been gathered some form of trend analysis will be necessary so that training sessions over a period of time may be analysed and comparisons drawn up. Some examination bodies may wish to see the evaluation forms.

...and finally...

Training skills take time and practice to develop. Patience is a virtue, just knowing about the subject matter and the needs of those on the receiving end of any training session will not make an effective trainer. WC Sellars and RJ Yeatman, in their book And Now All This (1932) wrote: "For every person who wants to teach there are approximately thirty who do not want to learn – much." If successful basic training skills are employed then perhaps for every person who wants to train there will be approximately thirty who will be able to apply much of what has been taught – all the time!

Further reading

- ♦ Coates, J (1984) *Practical Training*. Liss: Learnex Ltd;
- ♦ Hart, L (1991) *Training Methods that Work*. London: Kogan; and
- ♦ Rae, L (1995) *Techniques of Training*. London: Gower.

7 Resources To Use

"Soap and education are not as sudden as a massacre, but they are more deadly in the long run".
(Mark Twain 1835-1910)

Golden rules!

Resources? What are they? Basic dictionary definitions of "resource" include: inventiveness, means of support, stock that may be used, adapting things to one's purpose.

Resources and audio visual aids (AVAs) are a valuable contribution to any training activity. However, the golden rules are:

- ♦ they must be relevant to the trainees and training activity. For instance, do not show residential care workers who dish out food at the bedside hygiene practices in a cook-chill production plant, or bottles of cleaning chemicals which are not used in a particular premises (especially if it has a contract with another cleaning chemical company);
- ♦ the materials must be understood and accessible to minority groups;
- ♦ they must be up-to-date and compatible. What is the point in waving a copy of the General Food Hygiene Regulations 1970 or the Industry Guide for Retail premises in front of trainee managers who work in the baking industry? They will want to see an up-to-date copy of regulations which affect them and also will want to read the relevant industry guide;
- ♦ they should not discriminate on grounds of religion, sex, culture, ability, race or creed; and
- ♦ any advertising or promotion of a branded name should be low key so that trainees are not distracted by the advertisement messages, thereby failing to get the hygiene message.

From whichever source the training materials come they need to be presented in a format that is attractive to the trainee. Prior to selection it is important to:

- ♦ assess the material with regard to its relevance to the trainees' needs;
- ♦ consider the purpose for which it will be used;
- ♦ assess its appropriateness in terms of age, gender, and culture;
- ♦ assess its clarity and quality in terms of presentation; and
- ♦ assess the complexity of the language.

Think about:

- ♦ language barriers;
- ♦ special needs;
- ♦ hearing impairments;
- ♦ visual impairment (colour blindness, sensitivity to glare etc.);
- ♦ dexterity of trainees who have to handle it; and
- ♦ common allergic reactions (in the case of foodstuffs being used as a resource).

Senses

Trainees will respond to using all their senses at different relevant intervals throughout the training event. Taste, smell, sight, sound and touch can all be employed with some imagination.

Making contact

Use the following to make contact with resource providers:
- local telephone directories;
- Yellow Pages;
- internet, for example, www.caterer.com;
- colleagues;
- educational establishments;
- conferences and seminars;
- government agencies (such as the FSA);
- food and equipment suppliers;
- trade directories such as Caterer and Hotelkeeper's annual directory of products, services and information;
- publishers; and
- exhibitions.

Organisations

There are many organisations connected with training who can help with visual materials whether in the form of leaflets, posters, samples, etc. These include:
- FSA;
- Local Authorities;
- NHS Primary Care Trusts;
- Sector Skills Councils;
- Examination Bodies;
- Further and Higher Educational Establishments;
- Trade and Professional Associations;
- Consultants;
- Publishers; and
- CBT companies.

Having selected and used a particular resource it is essential to evaluate how effective it actually was. Appendix 1 has a summary of useful contacts which may be contacted to help with the provision of resources.

Audio visual aids? - look around you!

Purchasing materials can be expensive, and they do not always meet the needs of the trainees. Always seek permission to use equipment, materials, records and charts from the manager of premises where on-site training may be taking place. Think about taking photographs or videoing scenes that will enable the reinforcement of teaching points. Are the identified resources easily understandable? The trainee may have a different viewpoint or misunderstand the purpose of a resource. S/he will gain far more from a session where a range of audio visual aids are used to stimulate all the senses and the trainee has a chance to get involved in discussion. Language or learning barriers can quickly discredit an expensively purchased state-of-the-art resource if the trainer has not researched the needs of the target audience or practised using the resource.

Example used in this section:

- acetates;
- charts;
- documentation;
- boards;
- crosswords;
- photographs;
- cleaning equipment;
- homemade materials;
- candidates;
- disposable gloves;
- agar plates;
- computers;
- imitation foods;
- cassettes;
- handouts;
- booklets and leaflets;
- demonstration kitchens;
- PowerPoint;
- colour-coded material;
- internet; and
- training packs.

Acetates:

Acetates are used on overhead projectors. They can be made using your own materials and ideas, or there are a number of companies that produce them commercially. Don't be lulled into a false sense of security by thinking that acetates have to be used all the time. There is nothing worse for the trainees than to see a large pile of acetates sitting by an overhead projector, or a trainer insisting that every visual aid is an acetate. If you are making your own ensure that the wording is clear, colourful and that there is not too much information on them. Five to seven bullet points or a simple drawing are all that are needed. Advertisements around the edge of an acetate can be distracting.

Agar plates:

What better way than illustrating the microbial contamination of surfaces such as the back of a watch, heel of a shoe, dirty and clean fingers, spit, cough, raw and cooked foods, etc. than to use different agar plates? The problem with bugs is that they take time to grow unless an incubator is available. Trainers may find this form of resource suitable for a long term course run over three or five days. Warning: consider the Control of Substances Hazardous to Health (COSHH) Regulations 1999 before using these.

Candidates on a five-day Advanced Certificate in Food Hygiene were discussing microbiological contamination. As this was on day one of the course which was spread out over two weeks, the candidates were asked, under supervision of the trainer, to contaminate blood agar plates obtained from a hospital laboratory. The plates were then sealed after contamination and incubated at room temperature. Three days later the trainees were shown the results. In pairs they were given separate plates and asked to come up with specific food hygiene management controls to prevent the contamination occurring again.

Boards:

Flipcharts, dry boards and chalk boards can be used. Writing must be clear and legible. Uppercase lettering is preferable. This should be 3-5 cms high. Use of colour can help. Check the group to establish if there is any colour blindness. Any more than seven to eight teaching points on one sheet of paper or board will be too much for the candidates to take in.

Booklets and leaflets:

Some businesses produce their own booklets for their employees, whilst others prefer to purchase them from publications companies or examination bodies. Sometimes these are available in languages other than English. Publications are available from the FSA at little or no cost. Whatever is used ensure that it matches the language and learning abilities of the target audience.

Candidates:

Do not forget your most valuable resource – the candidates. Draw upon their experiences and seek solutions. Get them involved. For instance break them into groups. Ask each group to come up with a rhyme or rap on a topic such as personal hygiene – it's great for team building too! This is an exercise which has successfully been used in courses for supervisors such as the Intermediate Certificate in Food Hygiene.

Consider a kitchen brigade meeting. An executive chef insisted on a brigade meeting in a five star hotel kitchen every Monday. At each meeting he made the point that at least one of the kitchen staff would take it in turns to demonstrate a hygiene topic to his or her colleagues. Examples included the correct use of a probe thermometer, cleaning the seals on a refrigerator door and the correct use of disposable gloves.

Cassette recorders:

Trainees may find recording their thoughts about good or bad food hygiene practices useful. It may help them to avoid worries about concentrating on writing or spelling abilities. An alternative is to use CD players with relevant songs and extracts of stories.

Charts and graphs:

Be careful, as the trainees with poor numeracy or reasoning skills may misinterpret the information. For instance, a commonly used chart contains a graph of notified food poisoning figures for the UK over a number of years. Trainees may interpret the figures as very low, very high, going up, or insignificant when compared to the FSA's alleged 4.5 million cases of food poisoning per annum. The "official private" figure is closer to a million. It is important to note that the food poisoning notifications are not being used by the FSA to determine their 20% reduction - they are using laboratory isolates.

Cleaning chemicals and disinfectants:

The trainer will have to consider the implications of the COSHH Regulations 1999 before using chemicals. However, disposable wipes and empty bottles of sprays make the presentation more interesting. Don't forget soap and paper towels!

Colour-coded equipment:

What better way to demonstrate colour-coded equipment than passing cutting boards around the class?

Computers:

See the chapter about e-Learning and CBT.

Crossword puzzles:

Candidates with learning or language difficulties may find these off-putting. Crosswords may be useful for levels 2 and 3 trainees. They may be useful ice-breakers or can be used for revision purposes.

Demonstration kitchens:

These come in all shapes and sizes. The best place to train someone who works in a kitchen is in the kitchen. BUT, and it is a big *but*, before the training takes place the trainer will have to carry out both a risk assessment for health and safety under the MHSWR 1999, and a hazard analysis under regulation 4(3) of the Food Safety (General Food Hygiene) Regulations 1995.

Consider an alternative demonstration kitchen. A one-day course was run for 10 nursery school staff. The classroom used was in the school. There were plenty of imitation toy foods, and a toddler sized kitchen complete with oven, hob, dishwasher and fridge. These were ideal for getting key points across about practices in a kitchen.

Disposable gloves:

The trainer can demonstrate the correct use of gloves and things that go wrong with them, such as leaving them on a work surface, or stuffing them in a pocket, or most importantly, not washing the hands before putting them on.

Documentation:

If documents such as cleaning schedules, food safety policies and HACCP control charts exist, then show them to trainees. Where training takes place within a company or premises show the trainees the documents and posters relevant to that company or premises and not information from another business.

Food articles:

Cans of food, examples of high and low risk wrapped and unwrapped foods are visually stimulating and provide a focus for both the trainer and trainees. High-risk foods may start to smell if left in the training environment for too long. See imitation foods below.

Handouts:

These may be purchased commercially or produced in-house. The best handouts have relevant pictures and few words. If the written word is used ensure that all the trainees understand the content. The Plain English Campaign do provide a service to test the clarity of documents. All documents assessed by them are tested for:
- sentence length;
- line length;

- use of lists;
- good use of white space;
- clarity and size of fonts used;
- layout;
- correct grammar;
- correct spelling;
- correct punctuation;
- use of verbs; and
- use of personal reference words.

Contact the Plain English Campaign on 016363 744409, or visit their web-site at www.plainenglish.co.uk.

If you are producing your own leaflets and handouts be careful of copyrights. Also will the reader really understand what you have written? You may understand but, to use a newspaper analogy, are you a Guardian reader writing for the Sun or local press?

Considering the frequency of gobbledygook test. To do this:

- count a 100 word sample;
- count the number of completed sentences in the sample;
- divide the number of words by the number of sentences to give the average sentence length;
- add up the number of words with three or more syllables to give the percentage of long words in the sample; and
- add the percentage of long words to the average sentence length. This will give the test score. A higher score means a lower readability.

Homemade materials:

Materials designed by trainers for teaching purposes are an inexhaustible resource. For instance a laminated thermometer on an A2 size sheet can be effectively used to explain the relationship of bacterial growth to specific temperatures. The sheet can be attached to a flip chart. The thermometer scale is from minus 30 degrees Celsius to plus 140 degrees Celsius. On top of the laminate, and on either side of the thermometer are two strips of velcrose tape. One side is used for demonstrating everyday temperatures. These include: freezing point of water, boiling point, room temperature, body temperature, fridge and freezer temperatures, oven temperature. The other side is used for demonstrating the effects on bacteria (favourable temperature, slows down, dormant, dying, killed off and spore activation, etc.). Trainees are each given a cartoon relating to one of the everyday temperatures and asked to stick them on the board where they think they ought to be. On the other side the trainer can add the bacteria as s/he discusses the effects of temperature on bacteria.

Imitation foods:

Have you ever walked past a food shop to see lots of different breads or sausages hanging in what would otherwise be considered a place where they are exposed to a risk of contamination? Take a closer look. Imitation cooked and raw chickens, for example, can be used to demonstrate cross contamination – both direct and indirect. Various companies produce artificial or imitation food. Some of them are very realistic. Brie, steak pie, cooked and raw chicken, ham, kebabs, eggs, bacon, vegetable items, etc. The list is seemingly endless. But be warned - so is the price. Depending upon the budget, use play foods from children's toy shops or visit some magic/joke shops! Imitation or artificial foods can make perfectly adequate substitutes for raw foods. Some toy shops sell imitation toy foods. For better examples of imitation foods, specialist suppliers may be required.

Internet:

Although this has been mentioned before it is a highly valuable resource for downloading documents, leaflets, activities for exercises or ice-breakers, and self-directed learning programmes. The FSA site is improving – although try across the Atlantic and visit the USA's Food and Drugs Administration site for information. It is unacceptable that in the UK, food businesses have to pay for the Industry Guides to Good Hygiene Practice. Go elsewhere in the world and the advice is free. Trade associations, professional organisations, and food**link** have useful sites. The food**link** site at www.foodlink.org.uk has a wide range of really useful games, crosswords, wordsearches, quizzes, downloadable photographs of bacteria on various surfaces (especially hands), colouring activities, self-assessment tests, and other information which can be used for ice-breakers and throughout the course.

Photographs:

Trainees relate to familiar situations and therefore any visual material which enables them to think about their working practices and environment will be more meaningful. For instance, a series of pictures could be set up showing good and bad personal hygiene habits or food storage. The trainees are then divided into groups and asked to identify the good or bad practices shown in a particular photograph. Photographs of contaminated food stuffs, or of evidence used in recent prosecutions, can illustrate or enhance descriptions. If the trainees are from a catering background the photographs should be based on catering.

Posters:

Posters provide very good passive learning media whether shown in a training room or displayed in a staff room. However, they should never be left in one place for any more than two to three weeks. Any longer than that and the target audience may forget what the main messages are. This can be compared to the staff holiday postcards, which remain on notice boards, and no one can remember the content or sender! A good manager will take time to discuss the poster with their employees and carry out some form of post-discussion evaluation to assess whether there has been any behavioural change. When positioning posters ensure that they do not provide harbourage for pests. The target group must understand the language and pictures used on posters without causing offence. Before positioning any poster inform the employees about the purpose and use.

PowerPoint or OHP?

PowerPoint has started to replace the use of acetates and overhead projectors (OHPs). However, this is not always the case and depends on the purpose of the training session and the target audience. Whichever one is used the trainer must be aware of "Death by PowerPoint" or "Acetate fatigue"! These may occur by overuse and not allowing the trainees active participation during the training session. PowerPoint can be particularly effective for demonstrating the growth of bacteria by binary fission over the period of a particular training session. If acetates or slides are used there should be no more than 6 teaching points on each.

Presentation folders:

Some companies produce A4 or A3 sized free-standing presentation displays on subjects such as hazard analysis or cleaning. These are particularly useful for one-to-one training sessions or small groups.

A manager of a café had requested some one-to-one training to help clear up some misconceptions she had regarding hazard analysis. The trainer used a freestanding display folder to illustrate the key stages of a hazard analysis.

Induction Training: new employees were shown around a production kitchen. The trainer showed them where to wash their hands and how to wash them. Before going around the kitchen all the new employees had to demonstrate that they had been able to properly wash and dry their hands.

Press releases:

Newspaper and magazine articles add some reality and interest to discussion. But they must be up-to-date and relevant to the course. Some may be copied on to PowerPoint or acetate. Remember the gobbledygook test in the handouts section above? In 1980 the National Consumer Council carried out tests that showed that the following had these scores:

♦   The Sun   25
♦   Daily Mail   31
♦   The Guardian   39

Press releases also make good group work activities if used correctly. For instance in December 2001, a London morning paper carried a short piece saying that pork leaving the slaughterhouses was more likely to be contaminated with salmonella than beef or lamb. No facts were given or hygiene advice offered for consumers. In March 2002, the Consumer Association issued a press release stating that in a recent sample of 300 raw chickens obtained from supermarkets 16% were contaminated with salmonella. Again no practical advice was given to the reader about prevention of contamination and how to make the food safe to eat (nor, rather worryingly, was any mention made to indicate this figure was approximately 4 times lower than equivalent samples taken in the 1980s!). The candidates could be given the scenarios and asked questions about advice to consumers, cooking instructions, etc.

Publications:

There are many very well-written books, leaflets, and booklets commercially available from specialist publishers, examination bodies, and institutions. Some are translated into other languages apart from English. Many are targeted at specific groups such as managers, residential care workers or food production technicians. Use the appendix at the end of this book for guidance. There will also be publications located in the hotel or restaurant, production plant, or hospital, where the training is taking place. These could include cleaning schedules, instructions for equipment, documented HACCP or food hygiene policy statements.

Real life materials:

Real life plays a major part in successful food hygiene training. Trainees need something to link the theory to their role at work. Much of the information costs very little. Some of these have been mentioned in this text before. Menus, news articles, leaflets and documents relevant to the business can be used. Even cleaning materials, record charts, probe thermometers, gloves, aprons and boards have their uses. Use opened and unopened cans – what a better way than to demonstrate the purpose of expansion rings and the problems of seams?

Specimens:

Examples of dented cans or insects, baits, rodent droppings, gnawed foods and packaging, pest control books, and traps are very good for reinforcing teaching points.

Videos:

If using videos ensure that they are relevant to the trainees' working environment. Use parts rather than whole video films to re-emphasise particular points. Many companies produce videos that have pauses or breaks at suitable intervals to enable the trainer to use part or whole of the video. There is no rule that says that the whole video has to be shown. A good video should last no more than 15 minutes otherwise trainees will lose their attention. Sometimes, subject to performing rights and copyright permissions, extracts of food or catering scenes from TV programmes and cartoon films on tapes, or CD-ROMS can help to add humour – especially after a lunch break when trainees seem to have a shorter attention span than beforehand. Video films should never be used to substitute the role of the trainer. They provide reinforcement of teaching points. Before a video is used explain why it is being put on. After a film has been shown discussion about its contents should take place. Use questionnaires or set up work groups. The language should be suitable for the audience. In video film producers may put a limited shelf life on their videos by adding phrases such as "the pending/recently introduced legislation", or "in part two shortly to be produced" or " in the booklet which accompanies this video". In October 2002 the FSA sent a video to 300,000 catering businesses. It was part of the on-going food safety campaign. The eight-minute film illustrates bad practices in a café focussing upon cleaning, cooking, chilling and cross-contamination. Not a bad video if it is placed in the hands of a trainer first. The uneducated will not realise that the pink stuff (ultra violet light sensitive gel or dust) on foods and work surfaces is meant to demonstrate the spread of bacteria. A trainer will be able to explain before the video is shown what the candidates should look out for.

Wordsearches:

Ideal to help individuals to remember spelling of key words, and also to be used as a "filler" resource when there is an opportunity to break the ice or give trainees some refresher training. There are various free programmes available on-line for you to compile your own wordsearches. food**link** has downloadable word searches. They are fun to complete – but maybe not for the candidates who have languages other than English, special needs or learning difficulties.

An example of resource use:

The example given next is to demonstrate that a wide range of different resources can be used during a training programme. In this instance the course is a Foundation Certificate in Food Hygiene. The target audience and duration of the course for this example are of insignificance. Not all the suggested resources have to be used. It is up to the trainer to decide about the relevance and suitability of each.

COURSE SECTION	CONTENTS	RESOURCES
Introduction	Ice-breaker	Inviting the trainees to help themselves to tea
	Housekeeping	Pointing out health and safety signs, reading out housekeeping matters, enrolment forms, etc
	Introductions	Introductions in pairs
	Aims and objectives	Holding up specimen certificate. Using acetates or PowerPoint. Asking trainees to write down what they think will be in the contents of the course
Food Hygiene and Food Poisoning	Definitions of food hygiene, food poisoning	Trainees split into groups to come up with definitions using flipcharts. A video, such as the first four minutes of Hygiene the Movie part one illustrates food poisoning in a humorous way
	Importance of food safety and food poisoning	Examples of press releases and when food hygiene/safety has affected people
	Basic bacteriology	Agar plates, photographs of spoiled foods
	Key food poisoning bacteria	Handout summarising characteristics
	High risk foods	Imitation foods Canned food Uncooked and cooked rice Food containers
	Temperature control	Home made thermometer with common temperatures, and bacteria reactions to different temperatures Probe thermometer LCD thermometer Alcohol freezer thermometer
BREAK TIME		Ensure that there are food hygiene posters and photographs on the wall near the coffee area or at the back of the training room
Hazards and Contamination	Hazards	Assured safe catering laminated poster or Highfield.co.uk Ltd HACCP posters. Hazard spotting exercises are available

COURSE SECTION	CONTENTS	RESOURCES
	Contamination	Photographs of contaminated food, work surfaces and equipment. Chopping boards, tongs, cloths and other items of equipment are very visual. Imitation food can be used to demonstrate direct and indirect contamination.
	Personal Hygiene	Give each candidate a photograph of a "dirty" chef or a "clean" chef. Ask them to identify good and bad points. Use photographs of bacterial contamination on hands before and after washing, handling foods, etc.
	Fridge/Freezer storage	Photographs or drawings of fridges and freezers illustrate the key points. But also, the trainees could be split into two groups to draw up a list of rules.
	Stock rooms	Photographs or videos may be useful. Hazard spotting cartoons are available.
	General	To sum up this section use a video such as the FSA's video which demonstrates clean, cook, chill, and contamination.
	Exercises	Give the trainees different scenarios of food premises inspections and ask them to identify the risks of contamination and the advice they would give to rectify the situation, for example, notes from a sandwich bar, buffet, street market stall, private members club, restaurant kitchen, etc.
LUNCH		When the candidates are out to lunch leave some wordsearches, or FSA or food**link** leaflets on their workplaces. Do not forget to tell them once they reconvene to read the leaflets at a later date.
Post-Lunch session		To ease the trainees back into a food hygiene mode, show them a clip of a comedy video or a cartoon which demonstrates poor food hygiene in an entertaining way. There are tapes around which are inoffensive.
Cleaning and Disinfection	Cleaning Disinfection	Demonstrate this section using empty sample bottles, cleaning schedules, colour-coded cleaning equipment. There is a video called "A Clean Sweep" which could be used. (Highfield.co.uk Ltd)

COURSE SECTION	CONTENTS	RESOURCES
Pest Control	Rodents Insects Control	Either live or preserved specimens liven up a session. Droppings, traps, photographs and damaged food packaging or materials, fault-finding exercises can all be used to involve the trainees.
Waste Disposal		Models of wheelie bins, and photographs could be used.
Legislation		This session can be quite dry if too much legal jargon is used. Some video films are available but they may show scenes which are not relevant to some of the trainees. Industry Guides to Good Hygiene practice should be made available. Press releases of prosecutions and examples of notices could be shown or discussed with the trainees.
Summary		An interactive video is of use. Especially where there are different scenes and the trainees have to find faults or good practices for themselves. This helps with revision and to clear up any difficulties which may have arisen.

An example of use:

One imaginative training provider has a training room that has accessible tables and chairs for the trainees. On the side walls there are full-scale model kitchens and food rooms. These show good and bad hygiene practices, together with imitation foods. The candidates are encouraged to put items in the correct position or throw items away in a refuse bin. At the coffee/tea end of the room there is a wall full of photographs and a range of visual posters for the trainees to look at.

During the session on bacteriology, an on-going PowerPoint system is used to show the growth of bacteria during the whole session.

At the start of the day's events a fine invisible sprinkling of dust is used on the trainees' course programmes to illustrate cross-contamination at the end of the morning. The dust shows up in ultra-violet light. Before lunch break trainees are asked to put their hands in an ultra violet light reactive gel. They then go and wash their hands. Before eating the trainees put their hands under an ultraviolet light to show how effective their hand washing has been.

Further reading

Contact publishers and publications suppliers. Examples of companies and organisations producing food safety materials for training and research are listed in Appendix 1. Do not forget to use the internet to search for on-line publications – many of which may be downloaded free of charge. One such example of a website is www.catering-uk.co.uk which gives details of publishers of information in paper or internet format.

8 Choice of Courses and Trainers

"The more alternatives, the more difficult the choice." (Abbé d'Allainval 1700-1753)

Some issues to consider

"What do you want your employees and business to get out of a course?" If the only answer is "a certificate" then you seriously need to consider how this is to help them and the business. The course must be flexible enough to suit the needs of the business and be relevant to the work of the employees. Above all as a manager or supervisor it is important to realise that the responsibility for the training cannot lie solely at the door of the trainer. Supervisors and managers must be prepared to help with practical implementation and on-going supervision.

Some form of training needs assessment will be necessary to help determine what form of training should take place. An HACCP system will help here. Likewise some decision about post-course evaluation will be necessary. Are you sending individuals just to get a certificate because you believe that is what the law requires and have not considered the best form of training for the individuals to help your business, and perhaps their career development or motivation? Are you organising training because HACCP has helped to identify a problem? Will the course focus upon food hygiene and safety issues specific to the work of an individual or the role of a team within the business?

Which course?

In the 1980s the foundation level food hygiene courses had no formal recognition. This changed with new legislation, demands placed on the industry and external influences such as the EU. The format of delivery was rigid and there was little or no room for adapting the courses to the particular needs of businesses or employees. Managers were limited in the delivery of the courses and evaluation of the courses would often reveal the same strengths and weaknesses. Since the introduction of NVQs and SVQs, organisations such as the CIEH have only partially realised that delivery has to be more flexible. However, for the examination bodies, generating income may be far more important to some of them than actually helping food handlers and their employees in being able to demonstrate real change in food hygiene practices. Food hygiene training which provides a work-based qualification and proof of competence at work, is employment-led, not tied to a specific route of learning, and available to everyone, will be the order of the day in the near future.

The HtF provides support for organisations and businesses who wish to design and deliver training courses. It will also give advice on evaluation. For any training manager tasked with these roles the HtF is also an awarding body for NVQs/SVQs. Qualifications awarded by the HtF (where the Foundation Certificate in Food Hygiene is a necessary part of the underpinning knowledge) include, for example:

- Catering and Hospitality NVQ level 1 and level 2;
- On licensed Premises NVQ level 3 and 4;
- Craft Baking NVQ level 2 and 3; and
- Cleaning NVQ level 1 and level 2.

If the route is to be a QCA approved certificate course then contact one of the examination bodies listed below:

♦   CIEH;
♦   RSPH;
♦   RIPH; and
♦   REHIS.

Examples of the QCA approved courses broadly fall into the following categories including:

Level	Title	Awarding Body	Duration	Assessment	Entry Criteria
Level 1	Foundation Certificate in Food Hygiene	CIEH RIPH RSPH REHIS	6 to 9 hours	Multiple choice examination or oral examination	Nil
	Food Safety Foundation (CD-ROM)	RIPH	Minimum of 6 hours	Continuous assessment using a software programme	Basic computer keyboard skills
	Certificate in Essential HACCP Practice	RSPH	Minimum of 6 hours	Multiple choice examination	Level 1 food hygiene certificate is recommended
Level 2	Intermediate Certificate in Food Safety	CIEH RIPH RSPH REHIS	18-22 hours	Multiple choice or short answer examination	Not specified although each examination body may have its own criteria
	Intermediate Certificate in Applied HACCP	RIPH	18 hours	2 hour examination	At least a level 1 food hygiene certificate
	Intermediate Certificate in Hazard Analysis Principles and Practice	CIEH	12-14 hours	2 hour case study assignment at the end of the course	At least a level 2 food hygiene certificate
Level 3	Advanced Certificate in Food Safety	CIEH RSPH REHIS	30-40 hours	Two assignments and a written examination	Level 2 food hygiene certificate or equivalent knowledge

Level	Title	Awarding Body	Duration	Assessment	Entry Criteria
	Advanced Diploma in Applied HACCP Principles	RIPH	30 hours		Level 2 food hygiene certificate or equivalent knowledge
	Advanced Certificate in Food Safety	RIPH	30-40 hours	Assignments and examination	Level 2 food hygiene certificate or equivalent knowledge

N.B. The titles of the qualifications may be subject to change. Contact the examination bodies directly to establish the title of each required qualification.

Kogan Page Ltd have produced a really useful guide entitled British Qualifications. It is a complete guide to educational, technical and academic qualifications in Britain. The guide also has details about awarding bodies, colleges and universities. In addition it gives details of membership grades of institutions and associations. Visit www.kogan-page.co.uk.

Some food businesses and training companies produce their own courses and means of assessment. Schemes, such as the RIPH's Certification of Products, give in-house courses some validity and weighting.

With any design, delivery and evaluation of Foundation Certificate in Food Hygiene courses, employers and employees should be aware that the potential benefits gained from the learning process far outweigh the possible "sense of legal duty" (perhaps they may start to think in terms of a "moral" duty).

Evaluation of Foundation Certificate in Food Hygiene training has particular problems:

♦ trainee reaction (trainee has to respond honestly and positively);
♦ learning achieved (style of testing will vary according to the type of learning to be evaluated); and
♦ behavioural change (difficult to evaluate non-physical activities).

Candidates have been known to pass the foundation food hygiene multiple choice examinations without even attending formal training. This is no guarantee that they are safer food handlers. Even if they do attend the course and pass an examination, it is beneficial to observe their practices at some period after the course (this apart from anything else prevents complacency and evaluates the effectiveness of the training).

Proprietors and/or managers may make another decision altogether. This is to design their own form of training and assessment. There is nothing wrong with this so long as it may be demonstrated that the training given works to improve standards within the business.

But beware! A Hazard Analysis system is not a determinant of competence. Richard Sprenger makes the following recommendations in his paper **Is there a need to improve food hygiene training?** which is to be found at www.highfield.co.uk:

"If we are to ensure effective food safety training, I would suggest consideration of the following recommendations:

♦ we must provide incentives and encouragement to ensure the commitment of owners and managers to the benefits of food safety training and the effective supervision and guidance of trained staff. (The attitude of supervisors and the hygiene culture of an organisation must be positive to give the correct message to staff returning from food safety courses.) Too many food handlers are advised to ignore certain hygiene practices as being too expensive or time consuming;

- food businesses should implement food safety training programmes, which include standards for induction, awareness, formal, management and refresher training. The knowledge and skills required for each post should be documented. Regular knowledge and competency testing of all staff should be undertaken to ensure satisfactory performance and determine the need for refresher training;
- all accrediting bodies should carefully review their current courses and examinations to ensure the relevance of content and the appropriateness of their course regulations;
- stricter control must be exercised over the quality of registered trainers. A combination of adequate technical knowledge and good training skills is essential;
- all unnecessary jargon and scientific language should be removed from foundation courses and examinations;
- courses should, as far as practicable, be less generic and the content should be of specific relevance to those attending;
- training and courses should be subsidised by the Government to encourage:
  - training for short periods over several days or weeks. A six or nine-hour course held over one day does not produce the best results;
  - smaller class sizes so that training can be more specific; and
  - competency based training at the work place;
- the examination pass rate should be increased to a minimum of 75% and incorrect answers to essential questions should result in candidates failing the examination. Greater priority should be placed on effective training of managers and supervisors. It should be a legal requirement for high-risk food businesses to have at least one person on site who has the relevant qualification and experience;
- stricter control is required over the issue and use of certificates;
- increased emphasis should be placed on the importance of in-house competency based training and supervision;
- during inspections, authorised officers should assess the competence of food handlers by observations and questions, not by the presence of certificates on walls; and
- governments should provide consistent scientifically based guidance on good hygiene practice (preferably based on EU advice)".

Choosing a trainer

The choice of trainer to deliver training is more important than the quality and effectiveness of the training itself. During 1992-93, Roberts conducted a survey to establish the training and development needs of the industry. Out of 300 companies employing 18,000 staff he found that 60% used external providers to a reasonable degree and that the quality of the programme or trainer (usually based on previous experience) was a critical decider. Cost was not a problem (Roberts, 1993). All courses were continually evaluated.

Trainers are nearer to the shop floor than many proprietors think. Once a decision has been made about the type of course and the reason for training, just look around. Consideration of the following will help to make a positive choice:

- the reason for training – refresher, certificate, improvement in standards, etc;
- needs of the business – legal requirement, new product, change in menu, etc;
- needs of the trainees – refresher, language, ability to absorb information, further education, etc;
- needs of the manager – staff re-organisation, HACCP implementation, availability of staff, budget, etc;
- facilities – on-site vs elsewhere; and
- suitability of training on offer – generic or specific, classroom or workplace?

Once the above have been identified and assessed the manager will then need to consider:

- duration;
- time of delivery;
- references and previous experience;
- contracts;
- administrative arrangements;
- assessments;
- homework time; and
- post-course help and supervision for trainees, etc.

As for the trainer or training organisation, always take up references and consider:

- experience;
- cost;
- availability;
- course materials;
- language trainers;
- adaptability and suitability of course materials for your employees;
- criteria for delivery of courses on-site; and
- additional services such as pre- and post-course on-site evaluation.

Using trainers may not be as expensive as first thought. They can come in many different forms:

- **Mentor** – a colleague or manager who can work through a food hygiene training programme with an employee in their workplace. An example of this is the Restaurant Association's Food Safety Together programme. This is the Government's first funded food safety training programme at "induction level". It focuses upon positive safety improvements based on a "can do" rather than "must do" ethos. It promotes team work and helps to develop a food safety culture. A good manager will look around to see who in his/her team has had experience of a particular issue and how best they can share that knowledge with colleagues.

- **Manager/supervisor** – if they are doing their job properly they will make effective trainers. Their knowledge of the job and ability to identify and provide update or career development training is essential.

- **Registered trainer** – this may be someone already on-site, in a local authority, a consultant or a college lecturer who is registered to run specific national recognised food hygiene certificate courses. Check with the examination bodies to see who is a registered trainer. The difficulty with using an external trainer is that the courses and the materials may be too generic and off the shelf. For instance, some examination papers and materials may offend vegetarian businesses and vegetarian trainees. Some trainees may have difficulty in relating the information given during the training with what they actually can do at work. This is one of the difficulties in using an accredited exam. However, there are some trainers who will be pleased to design customised in-house courses and examinations.

- **Distance learning** – Some colleges and trainers run distance learning courses where the trainees use text books and work through materials in their own time. Practical implementation may prove difficult, unless a manager of supervisor helps.

- **e-Learning** – This comes in many forms such as using the World Wide Web, specific software packages such as those by Creative Learning Media and published by Highfield.co.uk Limited. Before purchasing any e-Learning materials check on support, social interaction, flexibility and possibility to adapt to the needs of the individual trainees.

The internet now opens a whole world of opportunities for managers to find trainers. A particularly good website is www.foodsafetytrainers.co.uk. The FSA at www.food.gov.uk also has details. These are by no means the only sites available. Try, also, websites of colleges and examination bodies.

Evaluation of trainers

Many of the examination bodies evaluate the trainers. This means that an assessor reserves the right to call in during the running of a course to assess the standard of training and code of conduct of the trainer. Good practice would be to consider how the trainer is to be evaluated by the trainees and the proprietor or manager of the business.

Important information for employers

The following may prove a useful A-to-Z check list for employers when deciding who to choose as a training provider, and what they may expect in negotiating a course to be run for their employees:

Advanced Level Assignments (where required): Candidates who attend Advanced level courses should complete their assignments at least 4 weeks before the scheduled examination date. Failure to do so may result in their business being invoiced for additional administration charges. Trainers should be able to give guidance about the layout of the assignments.

Attendance: Candidates must normally attend at least 80% of the training duration of the Advanced and Intermediate courses if they are to sit the examinations, and 100% of the duration of the Foundation course. Candidates cannot be expected to benefit from any training if they attend immediately after their shift ends or if they are to attend a shift straight after the course ends. Some employers may like to consider an hour's training before their employees start their work. They must not be made to take annual leave if they attend the health & safety or food hygiene courses. Hopefully trainers will be able to fit in around the needs of the food handlers and not the other way around – although when this is not the case some common ground has to be identified.

Certificates of Attendance: Candidates who complete the whole course but do not sit the examinations may be given a certificate of attendance by the trainer. The certificate should indicate the level of course attended, the syllabus followed, and the date of the course. It should not specify failure or discriminate against the candidate.

Comments about the Service: The training provider should welcome comments about the standard of training and any suggestions which may help improve the service. All candidates need to be given an evaluation form to complete at the end of each course and this usually involves preparation during the evening.

Complaints Procedures: Check the systems in place if a complaint is to be made about the training service.

Course Language Delivery: Courses may only be delivered in English. Check before sending your trainees on a course. Ask the trainer for any assistance available for trainees with languages other than English. Intermediate and Advanced level candidates should have an equivalent level of GCSE English language or Cambridge First Certificate (ESOL). Some trainers will give as much advice as possible to help candidates who lack key basic skills find an alternative training venue. Ask local authorities if they have a database with trainers who can run courses in other languages, or contact the examination bodies for advice about courses in other languages and for trainees with special needs or with learning difficulties.

Course Start Time: Candidates should turn up at least 10 minutes before the start of the course. Late-comers may be turned away by the trainer and no refund given.

Evening Work and Preparation: Advanced level and Professional Trainers Certificate course candidates may be given evening work. Professional Trainers Certificate candidates should note that they will be assessed on a short presentation on a topic of their choice.

Examinations: Foundation level candidates are given a multiple choice tick test paper at the end of their certificate courses. Oral exams may only be arranged for foundation level candidates. Intermediate level examinations may be multiple choice, and advanced course examinations are written. A scribe, who has had no training in food hygiene or health and safety, depending upon the examination, may be provided for a candidate with evidence of certificated special needs or learning difficulties, for example, dyslexia. Contact the relevant examination body concerned for advice. One major advantage of in-house exams is that candidates can go through the correct answers after the exam and no-one leaves the room thinking they have got the answer right when in fact it was wrong.

Invoice Payment and Contract: Is there a training agreement which commits the employer to a legally binding contract? What conditions are to be included in the conditions on the back of the training agreement?

Late Cancellations or Non-Attendance: These will render employers and candidates liable for payment of the full fee. Refunds may not be given.

Priority Bookings: Some training centres have priority attendance on the first available course(s) for clients within their area.

Refreshments: Lunch may or may not provided; however, tea and coffee should be available.

Service Standards: A copy of service standards leaflets may be available upon request.

Suitability of Courses for Candidates: Generally, Foundation level courses are open to all. However, Intermediate and Advanced level candidates should be able to demonstrate appropriate supervisory or management skills. It is important that Intermediate and Advanced level candidates respond to examination questions in an appropriate manner that reflects the added responsibilities or a team leader or manager.

Trainers: The trainers for the courses may be registered local authority officers, consultants, training contractors or college trainers.

Websites and Newsletters: Watch out for on-line food hygiene and standards advice which may also available. Likewise, check to see if the trainer provides any follow up information in the form of newsletters.

Joining instructions for employees
Are the trainees to be given any joining instructions? These should certainly include:
- title of course;
- venue and how to get there;
- start time; and
- date.

But also, they will include information such as:

Preparing for training
- Think about what they want to achieve - why are they attending and what do they hope to learn?
- Do some background reading into the subject. Discuss the course with their manager.
- Don't call work - make arrangements for someone else to handle queries.
- Participate - more will be gained from the training, if trainees ask questions and make contributions.
- Evaluate the training - comment on the variety of aspects of training.
- Update individual training records - a personal training record will have to be kept up-to-date.

On the day of training

♦ *Attendance:* ensure that the trainee arrives at least *ten minutes* before the start of the course. Late-comers may be turned away from the course. Partial attendance will stop the trainee from sitting the examination;

♦ *Dress:* usually casual but smart unless otherwise stated by their employer;

♦ *Refreshments:* coffee and tea (but not lunch) are provided during planned breaks for courses scheduled to be run in the training rooms. Lunch arrangements;

♦ *Duration:* course start and finish time;

♦ *Assignments for Advanced Courses:* Assignments must be handed in at least 4 weeks before the examination date. Failure to do so may result in an extra examination and administration examination fee being charged to the business;

♦ *Examinations:* Foundation level courses end with multiple choice tick tests (oral examinations may be arranged). Advanced level examination dates may be fixed by the awarding body. Re-sits are by arrangement and may incur additional fees;

♦ *Certificates:* Certificates are only given to candidates who successfully pass examinations at the end of certificate courses. Successful candidates receive their results and certificates eight to ten weeks after sitting the examination (providing the invoice has been paid);

♦ *Smoking Policy:* Smoking should not be permitted in any training room; and

♦ *Language:* The language of presentation and translation or interpretation provision needs to be outlined.

Course reading material and syllabus

Candidates are normally given reading material on all the courses. Intermediate and Advanced level food hygiene course candidates may be recommended to read, for example, the *Industry Guide to Good Hygiene Practice*. Available from the CIEH (020 7928 6006). Copies of the syllabus for each course should be available upon request.

After the course

Training records should be kept up-to-date. Continuous refresher training will be necessary. Further training will help with career development. Managers and supervisors, or owners of businesses, will find *Intermediate* and *Advanced* level courses more appropriate levels of training for the nature of their work activities.

Conclusion

The choices of trainers and courses are vital. But alone they will not improve food hygiene practice or provide evidence of competence. In-house courses and trainers have a very valuable place in training, just as accredited certificate courses and registered food hygiene trainers. Either option will have to be assessed as part of the training needs analysis, the hazard analysis and the nature of the business. Food hygiene is a 24-hour 365-days-a-year business. For the food handlers and owners of food businesses it should never stop. Unfortunately, too many managers of small or medium sized food businesses place the burden of training on external trainers. These managers have a responsibility to provide instruction and supervision of their employees once the courses are over. If the theory taught on the courses is not put into practice, then time, effort, and money spent on them will be wasted. Competency, not certificates, will help reduce customer complaints and improve food safety standards.

Further reading

♦   Roberts, J (1994) *Human Resource Practice in the Hospitality Industry*, London: Hodder and Stoughton; and

♦   HtF (2003) *Hospitality Network Directory*. London: Hospitality Training Foundation.

9 Computer Based Training and e-Learning

"To err is human but to really foul things up requires a computer." (Farmers' Almanac 1978)

An alternative training tool

Since the above anonymous quotation was published in 1978, the use and design of computers has come a long way. Only interactive computer based training (CBT) packages will help food handlers to learn using a computer at home or work, or in an internet café, but it is still no real substitute for practical application of the theory learnt. CBT may help individuals with special needs or language difficulties. However, the traditional approaches used in training should not be disregarded. CBT allows for interaction and so some trainees may not benefit from it – especially if they have had no basic training in the use of personal computers. The World Wide Web offers access to a huge store of food hygiene and safety information, and has details about training packages that may suit specific needs. The UK is the third largest user of information technology for learning and training programmes in Europe.

e-Learning and food safety/hygiene training

The following has been reproduced by kind permission of the RSPH. The original version of Euan MacAuslan's article first appeared in the Journal of the RSPH, December 2001, Vol 121, No 4, pages 213 to 219.

Surfing the net for information about food hygiene training availability in other languages reveals little in the way of assistance for ESOL food handlers. The ranges of websites do not give much information. The Department for Education and Skills, and the Food Standards Agency seem to have missed an opportunity by providing information and courses on-line in other languages apart from English – a sense of discrimination by information technology (IT). Some local authorities have sites which give information about food safety issues. However, the vast majority are in English.

Schools also use IT as a learning medium. Within secondary schools CD-ROM packages are available to help teach children about food hygiene. This was the result of a co-ordinated initiative involving the Department for Education and Skills, the Department of Health, the Health Development Agency and food hygiene examination bodies. For family-run food businesses this presents an obvious advantage especially where the parents do not speak good English. The children can pass on the theory in their own first language to their parents.

The difference between those using on-line learning and traditional learners (who attend training room based sessions) is that the former have to respond and interact differently to a learning programme by using IT skills in order to receive and gather information. The on-line learners have to offer evidence of their learning. With food hygiene CBT there has to be a proper evaluation of its effectiveness as regards change in practices within a food business.

However, at the beginning of the 21st century, there are still some of the adult population who are regarded as computer illiterate. Through no fault of their own they may not have received any IT training or have easy access to computers. It will therefore be necessary to consider a way forward which takes into account a range of abilities and learning methods.

Advantages and disadvantages of CBT

Advantages include:
- accessible courses at any time of day or night;
- no need to join a classroom-based or skills-based course;
- method of learning may suit some, but not all trainees;
- reduced resourcing costs; and
- contributes to lifelong learning and multi-skilling.

Disadvantages include:
- no interaction with a trainer for discussion;
- does not test competency;
- may present difficulties for trainees who do not have English as a first language, or are computer illiterate; and
- the programme may have a limited degree of flexibility.

The variety

Packages have been developed to assist trainees directly with food hygiene skills and indirectly by allowing trainees to develop their information technology skills, although some users learn more effectively from pen and paper, computers provide access to a whole new world of information and learning. Examples of use include:

- **Internet** – many local authority environmental health departments have food safety and hygiene web pages. These can be used for training purposes. An example is www.rbkc.gov.uk/foodhygieneandstandards. This site received a commendation award for the food**link**'s Food Safety Communications Awards in 2002. Or, institutions and organisations such as www.foodlink.org.uk for interactive food safety training. Try using a range of search engines to find food hygiene or food safety information. Be clear about what you are looking for and what you or your employees want out of it. Readers would do well to carry out their own research before deciding whether web-based training is for them.

- **CD-ROMS** – such as Food Safety Foundation produced by Creative Learning Media and Highfield.co.uk Ltd. This package has recently won awards and is used by over 300,000 food handlers. Highly interactive programmes such as these stimulate the learner through audio visual interaction in English and a range of other languages. Food Safety Foundation has received QCA approval as a vocational course, thus giving it some weight compared to not-so-user-friendly versions. In addition it has received a commendation from the RIPH. Another example of a CD-ROM may be obtained through www.qft.co.uk. More can be found on the internet.

- **On-line learning** – such as www.caterer.com which has produced "On-line Food Hygiene Training". This course provides an economical and flexible way of training individuals or large groups of staff quickly to recommended standards. The course in essential food hygiene is endorsed by the RIPH and successful participants receive a certificate on completion.

Government initiatives with e-Learning

There are various government initiatives covering e-Learning and its accessibility. Readers are advised to visit the websites below for more information.

University for industry:

Visit www.ufiltd.co.uk. The Ufi's learning services are delivered through **learndirect**, which provides access to innovative and high quality courses, over 80 percent of them on-line. **learndirect** will enable people to fit learning into their lives, learning wherever they have access to the internet - at home, at work, or in one of over 1500 **learndirect** centres. Successful completion numbers are quite low.

Learndirect:

www.learndirect-advice.co.uk about national learning advice.

The Labour Government at the start of the 21st Century set out its vision of "a learning society in which everyone, from whatever background, routinely expects to learn and upgrade their skills throughout life." Backed by Government, Ufi was created to make that vision possible. With plans to bring learning and skills into people's lives, Ufi developed the **learndirect** service to change the face of learning for hundreds of thousands of people, enabling them to :

♦ learn for fun or work;
♦ gain knowledge and skills to enhance their employability;
♦ take control of their future; and
♦ improve the competitiveness of their business.

National grid for learning:

Visit www.ngfl.gov.uk. The National Grid for Learning (NGfL) is a gateway to educational resources on the Internet. The NGfL provides a network of selected links to web sites that offer high quality content and information. Whether learning, supporting, teaching or managing, there are resources on the NGfL for all.

UK online:

UK online centres are for people who have limited or no access to skills in using new technologies. The centres will help people to develop the skills to use the Internet to access information, send e-mail using a PC, mobile phone, digital television or games console (please note not all centres will have the same facilities), and explore the opportunities that new technologies offer such as for further learning and updating skills.

The UK online centres are based in communities and will enable everyone in England who wants it to have access to the Internet and e-mail near to where they live. It could be in an Internet Café on the High Street, in a public library, in a college, in a community centre, a village, a mobile centre, or anywhere available to the public. They have been designed to meet the needs of local people who have low or no Information Communication Technology (ICT) skills or access to ICT.

UK online is a major government initiative that makes sure that everyone has access to the Internet. As well as providing access to the Internet and e-mail, support from staff in the centres will be on hand to help people to explore opportunities for further learning through ICT.

The Government is encouraging the population to take advantage of the rapid growth in computer technology and accessibility. **learndirect** seeks to make a very wide range of courses available in the home, community centres, educational establishments, internet cafés, workplaces, etc. It offers individuals a dual learning activity for their own personal self development. The first is learning about a particular topic, such as food hygiene on-line, and the second is improving computer and keyboard skills through the use of multimedia packages.

Adult learning partnership:

This is an organisation which can help employees and individuals (with funding support) improve their IT and keyboard skills before moving on to using e-Learning and food safety/hygiene training. Visit www.adultlearningpartnership.co.uk.

Developing an e-Learning strategy

The following has been reproduced by kind permission of Richard Taylor, Creative Learning Media Ltd. E-mail: richardtaylor@creativelearningmedia.com

e-Learning is the delivery and/or management of training or learning using computers. The delivery process may involve a corporate Intranet, the Internet (World Wide Web), an internal network, CD-ROMs, e-mail or any other electronic media.

Also referred to as:

- ◆ OL - Online Learning;
- ◆ CBT/L - Computer Based Training/Learning;
- ◆ MBT/L - Multimedia Based Training/Learning;
- ◆ TBT/L - Technology Based Training/Learning; and
- ◆ WBT/L - Web Based Training/Learning.

e-Learning, usually when it was referred to as CBT, first appeared over 20 years ago. Early CBT consisted of simple "book-on-a-screen" type resources with text-based questions. It was neither effective nor popular with trainees (or most Human Resources (HR) personnel) and mainly served to fuel the nightmare vision of the future where grey-faced people stare into computer screens all day with little or no human interaction. It also led to the general concern, that still survives to this day, that CBT will take the "human touch" away from training delivery. Fortunately, today's e-Learning reality is very different. Today's leading edge e-Learning programmes consist of visually compelling learning media including animation, video, simulated workplace environments and a challenging, fully interactive narration. The programmes are instructionally designed to promote the smooth operation of the three key phases of human information processing - attention, comprehension and retention/recall. Pre-training assessments enable each learner to receive individually tailored tutorials, which precisely target specific knowledge gaps, increasing learning effectiveness and dramatically reducing the average time needed to accomplish each learning goal. Today's e-Learning programmes are designed to combine strategically and seamlessly with traditional training methods. Far from taking away the human touch, they make the time invested in recruitment, on-job coaching and classroom style training even more productive. Effective learning and people development programmes are increasingly seen as vital to achieving business goals. Growing sales, improving customer service, and complying with legislation are all much easier to achieve with a well-informed, highly skilled and motivated workforce. A key business strategy for many corporations is to create a culture of learning within their organisation, where people want to learn and are able to learn, and can thus fulfil their full potential. Achieving this goal requires everyone in an organisation to have free access to an effective learning environment. This environment must, in turn, facilitate "just-in-time" training, delivered where it's needed, when it's needed, on demand. Good e-Learning solutions, when combined with traditional training techniques, can provide such a learning environment.

When assessing the feasibility of e-Learning solutions, the following costs should be considered:
- developing e-Learning programmes, and/or licensing/customisation of off-the-shelf solutions;
- developing/licensing a Learning Management System (LMS);
- new hardware/hardware upgrades;
- delivery and distribution - e.g. CD-ROM replication or lines cost if delivering via Intranet;
- technical support;
- internal marketing and promotional costs; and
- future programme development, update and upgrades.

The biggest cost of any learning or training programme is the learner's time. e-Learning reduces this cost in several ways:
- the training is delivered in the workplace - no travel time, or overnight stays;
- pre-learning assessments - no repetitive learning;
- individually paced learning - never too fast or too slow;
- learning in bite-sized chunks - higher attention levels, higher efficiency;
- learn during any spare time in the normal working day/shift; and
- just in time - learn as and when needed, not in advance.

Other cost savings include:
- reduced trainer costs - trainers can focus on other learning goals;
- reduced training administration costs;
- reduced certification costs (especially for Food Safety and Health & Safety training);
- no training room and facilities hire;
- no travel or accommodation costs;
- no consumable training materials costs (folders, handouts, stationery etc); and
- no need to replace worker for the day in the workplace.

The benefits of e-Learning solutions can be:
- accessed 24 hours a day, 7 days a week;
- accessed by everyone (including shift and part-time workers);
- individually tailored to the needs of each learner;
- the ongoing cost of training is typically reduced by 40 - 90%;
- put another way, up to 10 times as much learning can be achieved on the same budget;
- learning can be automatically managed and evaluated across an entire organisation, including:

- analysis of who is learning what, when, where and how;
- comparison of pre- and post-learning assessments; and
- evaluation of the system to enable continuous improvement.

The early feasibility study stage is likely to require the co-operation of several internal personnel from the HR, IT, and operating departments.

The formation of this "Strategy Team" is often the first stage in establishing an e-Learning strategy. Their aim is to source information and obtain answers to the initial questions that will arise. Later, the team will be instrumental in gaining wider support for the project as it develops.

Initial tasks will depend on the culture and needs of the business, but may include:

- identifying learning goals as possible solutions to business goals;
- identifying hardware availability/requirements;
- identifying delivery methods - intranet, CD-ROM, etc;
- investigating off-the-shelf vs bespoke solutions;
- identifying LMS requirements;
- identifying dependencies on internal and external personnel and resources;
- producing cost vs. benefit analysis; and
- making the business case for e-Learning.

A diverse range of skills, knowledge and experience is needed to develop effective and credible e-Learning solutions.

A well-structured project development system must be followed to ensure that the project is delivered on time and on budget without compromising on quality.

The best possible development system is one which facilitates effective team work and communication, imposes tight time and budgetary controls and encourages a high level of individual and group creativity.

The principle behind a sound development process and comprehensive test schedule is to provide an accurate solution at the outset that will need a minimum amount of maintenance.

It is essential that e-Learning programmes are based on accurate, up-to-date, information. They must also be relevant and credible in the mind of the learner. Some e-Learning materials betray the fact that the producers had only a superficial knowledge of the subject matter and the practical implementation of the desired working practices.

Producers, instructional designers and multimedia developers should all have sound knowledge and experience of the subject matter to ensure an effective development process from initial design and script to finished e-Learning product. In addition, the development team should have access to SMEs, particularly during the high-level instructional design and review stages.

An overall structure should be agreed based on the identified learning goals. This will consist of a series of learning modules, each of which might represent, for example 20 - 40 minutes of learning time. Each module will have clearly defined learning objectives.

Each module will culminate in a formal assessment (Mastery Test) that will verify and record the achievement of the overall learning objectives of that module.

Each module will be further subdivided into a series of sub-topics or "learning events". These will each have a corresponding required learning outcome linked to the overall learning objectives of the module.

Learning outcomes should ultimately be in the form of working practices that the learning programme needs to impose on the business.

The underpinning knowledge necessary to achieve the learning outcomes and objectives will need to be established and documented.

The documentation of the above for every sub topic and module of the learning programme will form the Content Specification.

Effective e-Learning programmes promote the smooth operation of the key phases of human information processing - Attention, Comprehension and Retention/Recall. This ensures predictably good learning outcomes.

The quality of the mechanism used to transfer new knowledge from working memory into long term memory determines the ability to recall the knowledge when needed. Knowledge should be linked to its future use through realistic and relevant exercises and simulations. Effective e-Learning programmes ensure that learning is an active role through self-pacing content that is delivered via a series of learning activities with immediate feedback. This creates a positive, credible learning environment, where users believe they can learn and want to learn.

Achievement of learning outcomes can be ensured and verified by frequent exercises and interactive simulations throughout each module.

The first stage of instructional design is the production of a high level storyboard based on the Content Specification. This document consists of a draft script and (usually text only) description of each learning event. Media requirements such as video, photography, graphic design and illustrations are identified and described. The high level storyboard is further developed into a graphical storyboard consisting of a sketch of each screen. A script and a detailed description of how the user will interact with the content accompany each sketch. Additional storyboards are required for video, animation and virtual reality sequences. Once reviewed and agreed, these detailed storyboards will serve as the requirement specification for the media producers, graphic designers and multimedia programmers.

The aim of the review is to ensure that the proposed design conforms with all design requirements. The review is an opportunity for the design team to discuss the proposed design and agree amendments if needed. This will ensure a minimum of later redevelopment.

The task of the LMS is to manage the delivery of learning content and track usage and record performance statistics.

A well-designed LMS can provide the following functionality:

- recording of core user profile details - name, ID, password, date commenced, status (certified/not certified/in-training), date passed mastery test, number of attempts, duration of learning, average duration of mastery tests;
- pre-learning assessments can determine the existing knowledge of each learner. The LMS can precisely identify and target individual knowledge gaps, significantly reducing the time required to achieve each desired learning outcomes;
- identify, track and report on the use of the online training product and assessment completion, at the area, site and individual level. It may also account for the progress of all users even if they change locations and provide an overview of the performance across the whole estate;
- automate the allocation of a unique ID related to the individual's role, site and area; and
- identify and report which employees are due for a re-test based on an administrator entering a "dateline" parameter.

The LMS can be documented and developed to enable swift integration with any other web-based business system. The system may be accessed through any computer running an Internet browser that can access the LMS home page on the server.

Critical success factors

If CBT is to be a success, the following will have to be taken into account:

♦ clear learning objectives, directly related to business goals;

♦ accurate, relevant and credible content;

♦ high quality instructional design, focused on learning outcomes;

♦ high level of interactivity, interest and challenge;

♦ well marketed internally with support at all levels; and

♦ constantly evaluated and improved.

Innovative kitchen training

During 2002 a range of interactive on-line learning materials were produced. The National Learning Network (NLN) at www.nln.ac.uk have produced interactive programmes which support certain elements of NVQ/SVQ level 2 Food Preparation and Cooking by providing underpinning knowledge. There are over twenty different titles of the learning units, some of which include:

♦ harmful bacteria;

♦ symptoms and causes of food poisoning;

♦ personal hygiene;

♦ food contamination;

♦ storage of food;

♦ cleaning;

♦ premises and equipment; and

♦ control of pests.

The next steps

Before rushing out to purchase software or signing up to on-line CBT consider, for example, some of following:

- ♦ read and research the most suitable product for you, your business and your employees;
- ♦ seek out references and ask other proprietors if they have used CBT for food hygiene training;
- ♦ ask software companies for free trials;
- ♦ carry out a pilot study;
- ♦ consider the backup you will need and who is to provide it;
- ♦ the learning environment could be a domestic or business computer, or somewhere such as a community centre or internet café;
- ♦ who is going to provide technical back up for candidates and the business?
- ♦ is this form of training value for money and how available will it be?
- ♦ some employees may need basic computer skills training before being expected to gain the benefits from technology;
- ♦ who and what are you going to evaluate?
- ♦ how will competency be assessed? and
- ♦ what will be used for refresher or other form of suitable food hygiene training?

Some types of funding such as European Social Funding may be available via the local Learning and Skills Council. The funding includes projects for training 14-to-19 year-olds, training people already in work to improve their career prospects, assisting individuals with basic and/or key skills, training unemployed individuals to set up on their own as a business or to gain work experience, etc. QCA accredited courses such as those offered by the CIEH, RIPH and RSPH may attract funding from the Learning and Skills Council.

10 A Lesson For The Future

"We should all be concerned about the future because we will have to spend the rest of our lives there." (Charles F. Kettering)

Where next?

This final chapter is intended to give readers a brief insight into what happens around the world, and what could happen in the UK. It leaves them to draw their own conclusions about what could be termed as effective food hygiene training. They then need to consider what could, or should be done in the future for the UK to provide effective and meaningful food hygiene training.

Governments and food safety professionals around the world have developed, and will no doubt continue to develop, food hygiene training and food safety strategies. Food poisoning is a global issue. There may be as many 1500 million cases per annum. Whilst the UK insists on publishing notified cases of food poisoning, in addition to estimated totals, it is interesting to note that Holland and France, for example, do not. Perhaps there is a moral to be learnt from this: "The more you tell people about something, the more they will worry about it" (Anon).

What is to happen in the future, and is there a role for food hygiene training? Most certainly, but not in its current mode. Policies that affect food safety and lifelong learning strategies have to work in partnership. Not, as the UK has at the moment, where attainment of a certificate in the eyes of accreditation bodies such as the QCA and funding bodies such as the Learning and Skills Council seems to be more important than practical implementation which in turn contributes to improved demonstrable food safety standards. The priority should not be to ensure a food handler ends up with a food hygiene certificate just because they have passed a test. The priority should be to ensure that the whole population understand their role and responsibilities to ensure that food poisoning does not happen in the home and in commercial businesses. Training (in its true meaning), not just education, is required.

To do this the legislators will have to define training requirements in a manner which enforcement officers really understand and to enable food business managers or owners to demonstrate practical implementation. The enforcers themselves will need considerably more training than at present to enable them to assess what type of training is required, and whether it has served the purpose relevant to the activities within a particular food business.

> W.E Hickson (1803-1870) wrote:
>
> *'Tis a lesson you should heed,*
> *Try, try again.*
> *If at first you don't succeed,*
> *Try, try again.*

So-called civilised countries are *trying* to protect their nationals in a whole range of ways. Students and postgraduates, governments, consumer associations and others have written books, papers, theses, strategy documents and commissioned research into evaluations of the effectiveness of food hygiene training. Innumerable conferences and seminars have taken place. But how much of it actually works and what benefits derive from it? Is more research the answer or is some research of published material now required from which a strategy and statutes can be drawn up? The reader may like to consider: "how many more lessons are needed until the future of food hygiene training ensures the protection of the consumers?"

European Union member states should, in theory, be following the same directives regarding food safety standards and employee hygiene. Using the world wide web will give a greater insight into these and of food hygiene training requirements and advice elsewhere in the world. Brief comments are given below about Australia, Canada, Ireland, and the USA:

Australia and New Zealand

The Australian Food Authority has prepared the following:

Food Safety: Guidance on skills and knowledge for food businesses
Advice for food businesses on the skills and knowledge requirement of Food Safety Standard 3.2.2 Food Safety Practices and General Requirements.

The guide is designed to assist owners of small food businesses understand the legal requirement for skills and knowledge in food safety and food hygiene. The Food Safety Standards require food businesses in Australia to make sure that food handlers and supervisors of food handling operations within their business have skills and knowledge of food safety and food hygiene for the work that they do. The guide is not legally binding. The contents are in two parts. The first covers skills and knowledge - an introduction. The second covers a guide to skills and knowledge needed by food handlers. The guide is well written and straightforward to interpret, unlike the UK's Industry Guides to Good Hygiene Practice.

For further information on the Food Safety Standards and other regulatory matters, visit www.foodstandards.gov.au or www.foodstandards.govt.nz.

(Acknowledgement for the above is given to Lydia Buchtmann, Program Manager Public Affairs Food Standards Australia New Zealand)

Canada

The Canadian Partnership for Consumer Food Safety Education is a public/private partnership that was created to educate consumers about their role in food safety. This site is meant as a tool to help the Partnership with its goal of reducing the incidence of foodborne illness in Canada. The Food Retail and Food Services Regulations 1999 require at least one person in every food retail business to hold a hygiene training certificate. Little advice is available about competency. Visit www.cfis.agr.ca/english or www.inspection.gc.ca for details.

Ireland

The Food Safety Authority of Ireland's aim is to protect consumers' health by ensuring that food consumed, distributed, marketed or produced in Ireland meets the highest standards of food safety and hygiene. The Agency has constructed a database of training courses on food safety and hygiene that are currently running in Ireland -"Food Safety Training Courses". These courses are aimed at all food handlers and those working directly in the food industry. The database outlines the agency responsible, contact names for further information and details of the courses. The transfer of knowledge and understanding to the work place is seen as vital. Certification alone does nothing to determine or provide evidence of competency. A national guide about food safety training provides a benchmark about what is expected, the clearly defined responsibilities of the proprietor, together with general advice, skills standards and checklists. The Skills Standards have been agreed with industry, enforcement officers and training providers. They allow for diversity in training provision and are recognised and used by the National Qualifications Authority. This is a forward-thinking approach which really needs to be considered in the UK.

Details may be obtained from The Food Safety Authority of Ireland, Training Compliance, Abbey Court, Lower Abbey Street, Dublin 1, Telephone: 817 1376, or visit www.fsai.ie

USA

The Food and Drugs Administration (FDA) has a very large website packed full of information for consumers, proprietors, food handlers and trainers. There are also wide ranges of links to sites which affect industry bodies, individual states or campaigns.

For example, www.foodsafety.gov is described as the "gateway to government food safety information". The range of languages other than English in which hygiene information and training advice can be found is phenomenal compared to the UK. Food safety programmes and activities for food, hospitality and retail, etc are available.

One of the links is to the Food Safety Training Education Alliance (www.fstea.org). This is an alliance intended to improve food safety training and education at the retail level. It covers retail food, food service, vending, institutions, and regulators. One of the goals is to "remove barriers to communication by facilitating information exchange, strengthen communications networks and alliances, and co-ordinating collaborative projects." There is a National Food Safety Educators' Network. www.ednet-l@foodsafety.gov is an electronic newsletter from the FDA that provides food safety activities to educators and others concerned about food safety. It is accessible free of charge in the UK.

Certification programmes in the USA conform to certain standards for validity, reliability and legal defensibility. Currently there are four recognised test forms. The following incorporate an examination:

♦ **ServSafe** - developed by the Educational Foundation of the National Restaurant Association.

♦ **Certified Food Protection Professional (CFPP)** - a credential developed by the Dietary Managers Association.

♦ **National Certified Professional Food Manager (NCPFM)** - Experior Assessments, LLC, administers the NCPFM exam.

♦ **Certified Food Safety Manager** - offered by the National Registry of Food Safety Professionals, Inc.

But don't stop there! Sweden and Japan, for example, are other countries that have realised the importance of food safety and the value of food hygiene training to improve standards. Assessment of their success is difficult to measure, but the UK could now consider looking beyond the EU for inspiration.

European Union

Much of the FSA's work is governed by European legislation. During 2000, the European Commission put a proposal for the establishment of a European Food Safety Authority forward. The Authority will be the key to a more strategic approach towards food safety in Europe. With regard to training, over the next few decades the Authority may well lay the framework for the future of statutory food hygiene training in the UK. Visit www.efsa.eu.int for full details about the work of this authority.

What could happen in the UK?

The UK is slow to respond with positive commitments to do something about food safety promotion compared to, say, what is happening in the USA. The British write papers, carry out research and hold conferences. Unfortunately there is little real national will to take the bull by the horns and give it a nationally agreed shake. But even advancements in food safety in the USA have not done much to reduce the 5,000 deaths from consumption of contaminated food which occur each year. Nor have they stopped at least one in every ten from seeing their doctor with an intestinal infectious disease.

For years, the five examination bodies in the UK did not speak to each other about a unified approach to food hygiene training and certification. Now there is some form of dialogue and realisation that uniformity in standards is not only important if QCA accreditation is to be granted, but also to help the trainees and their employers who send them on courses. Unfortunately the QCA and LSC still view certification as more important than a measurable change in behaviour. Perhaps they, along with the FSA, should seek to remove food hygiene training certificates from individuals and proprietors if standards do not improve in a business within a given period. The Irish system of emphasis on competency rather than possession of a certificate is to be commended. With the pending introduction of EU HACCP Directives, perhaps the FSA will consider this way forward when introducing the frame work for statutory HACCP training for managers and supervisors.

food**link** is promoting food hygiene education amongst consumers with events such as National Food Safety Week, and its excellent website (www.foodlink.org.uk). But it needs to model itself on the USA and Canadian idea of a having a national food safety month which involves both consumers and food businesses by focusing upon key issues.

Perhaps now is the time to establish a UK Food Safety Education Partnership. The FDA in the USA funds the Food Safety Training Alliance. Free membership gives members access to relevant websites, training material production news, and considerable information about how to train non-English-speaking food handlers. Visit www.fstea.org. A very wide range of organisations, examination bodies, businesses, and agencies have various diverse interests in the way food hygiene training is and should be conducted in the UK. There is no single partnership or organisation which co-ordinates alliances with these interested parties.

The potential exists to develop a UK Partnership for Food Safety Education committed to improving the accessibility, availability and effectiveness of food safety training in the UK. The objectives would be to:

♦ form partnerships with industry, education, health, consumer, trade, and enforcement agencies, to share food safety education materials and conduct joint education activities in order to share resources and expand the reach of the partners;

♦ form a partnership of food safety education expertise; and

♦ develop multilingual communication techniques targeted to specific groups to overcome communication barriers faced by trainers and food handlers.

A diverse membership is envisaged, with representatives coming from organisations such as: Government agencies, accredited examination bodies, industry and trade associations, retail food sector, catering businesses, NHS, hospitality and leisure premises, education establishments, business advisor groups, registered trainers, accredited examination bodies, local authorities, HM Forces, and consultants.

An evaluation would be required of various fund raising options including grants, EU and other public funds. A proportionate contribution from members who are likely to benefit may be considered as well.

If there is enough interest in developing a partnership the first tasks would be to:

♦ discuss, agree and prioritise the aims and objectives of the partnership;
♦ discuss and agree how these goals are best achieved;
♦ co-ordinate all publicly funded training initiatives on food safety;
♦ agree resources to address one or many of the current food safety training issues; and
♦ produce effective methods to improve food hygiene standards amongst the general public.

The public as well as food handlers should not be forgotten in any national food hygiene training strategy. Food handlers are subject to legislation. The public will require food hygiene education at school as a life skill and a social responsibility, not only in terms of preventing food poisoning at home, but also in how to accurately report food hygiene concerns observed in food businesses. In addition, improving access and increasing availability to computer based training will provide an opportunity for food hygiene training at all levels and for all walks of life.

Publishing (although somewhat controversial) risk assessment scores on the internet of food premises inspected by local authorities may help to raise standards and competition amongst businesses a stage further. These may be open to misinterpretation by the public and appeals by businesses for damaged reputations. If this information were published it should highlight training. A voluntary national award scheme must encourage the industry to open up its management strategies rather than to shy away from its statutory responsibilities.

To quote W.E. Gladstone (1809-1898) "You cannot fight against the future. Time is on our side." The human race can, in terms of food safety, fight against the future, especially if it is a fight to reduce risks. Time is not on our side if the matter is to be effectively resolved through relevant and effective food hygiene training.

GS Wilson, head of PHLS, in 1955 wrote: "In the communal kitchens, practices have been taken from the home which, though unobjectionable when applied to small quantities of food, present dangers when large masses of food are being handled. Water- and milk-borne disease, which have been the bane of mankind in the past, are being replaced by food-borne disease." Many businesses still require convincing that food hygiene and general cleanliness make sound business sense. They need persuading that high standards should be the natural "norm" rather than a legal minimum. Enforcement will need to be pitched at the right level throughout the UK. Also, the Chancellor of the Exchequer would do well to provide businesses with tax incentives for proper food hygiene training (which includes practical competency assessments). Money spent here may well mean a saving for the National Health Service and enforcement agencies who end up spending taxpayers' money on treating and/or investigating food poisoning outbreaks.

Networking will increase awareness

A little known fact, or perhaps advantageous fact, is that trainers who register with accredited examination bodies or other institutions (and in certain circumstances, some level 2 or 3 trainees) may apply for various grades of membership. The advantages include receipt of:

- membership status;
- journals or newsletters;
- details of seminars and conferences;
- possible discount for purchase of materials and publications;
- invitations to special events;
- opportunities to network with other food safety professionals, trainers and technicians;
- joining trainers' forums or user groups; and
- the chance to keep up-to-date with food safety issues, legislation and training techniques.

In addition, food clubs or forums run on a partnership basis with businesses, local authorities and other organisations help managers to exchange information and learn about new ideas which they can pass on to their employees.

A Food Safety Forum will provide an opportunity for businesses operating in an area to meet together and exchange ideas between themselves, guest speakers and with officers from local authority Environmental Health Departments. Successful forums are held in several areas in the UK such as The Food Club in North West London. The Club was formed in September 1996 and is a member of the London Chamber of Commerce and Industry and the North West London Chamber. Visit www.thefoodclub.org.uk for further details.

Forums or clubs have helped to break down barriers between enforcement agencies, organisations and food premises. Guest speakers from agencies and associations may be invited. Topics at meetings include subjects such as:

- purpose of food safety forums;
- addressing food hygiene training in other languages;
- ESOL food preparation courses;
- how to get the best out of future forums;
- product promotion;
- changes in EU legislation;
- HACCP; and
- potential forum hosts.

Terms of reference for the forums may include:

Objectives:

- to act as an open forum for two way discussion on food safety issues between local authorities and representatives from local businesses; and
- to act as a focal point for the exchange of views and information relating to food safety.

Membership:

- representatives from local food businesses, consultants, trainers, and the local authorities' Environmental Health Departments;
- forum meetings will be accessible to at least 15-30 businesses per meeting; and

♦   membership should aim to include representation of ethnic and other minority groups from businesses.

Operation:
♦   the forums will meet on a quarterly basis in differently hosted venues;
♦   the forums' members will agree upon the choice of initiatives and project areas;
♦   current local and national thinking and priorities will inform all work;
♦   the forums are a non-party political body; and
♦   the forums will endeavour to ensure equal opportunity for everyone irrespective of any individual's physical ability, age, religion, race, gender, etc.

Training the employees of tomorrow

Some local authorities run education business partnerships which involve meetings between local authorities, schools and businesses. The Government aims to provide all young people with a wide range of high quality, relevant, structured experiences of work throughout their school careers. These experiences will help raise standards of achievement, increase motivation and attendance, develop key skills and attitudes, and prepare young people more effectively for adult and working life. Visit your local authority website or www.dfes.gov.uk/ebnet. Alternatively, visit The National Education Business Partnership which is the umbrella organisation and national voice for 138 Education Business Partnerships working in the 11 regions. It is a membership organisation with a growing number of Associate and Business Members. Their website is at www.nationalebp.org

Food hygiene education takes place in secondary schools for GNVQs. It also appears on the national curriculum at primary level for personal, social, and health education. The British Nutrition Foundation www.nutrition.org.uk and food**link** www.foodlink.org.uk have resources for training in schools.

The Education Act 2002 gives schools a wider remit in the way they deliver the curriculum, and to some extent what they include in the content. Teachers are encouraged to use a range of methods and varieties of resources to involve the students in learning. Computer based learning is being increasingly used in the classroom. With this in mind food hygiene programmes such as those produced by Highfield.co.uk Ltd and Creative Learning Media are becoming increasingly common.

Food safety subjects taught at various primary and secondary levels include, for example:
Food safety and hygiene need not be taught as separate subjects. They can be integrated into other key topics. For example:

Key Stage 1 and 2	Personal hygiene, use of aprons, hand and hair washing
Key Stage 2	Personal hygiene, use of cleaning chemicals, symptoms of food poisoning
Key Stage 3	Food hygiene, basic bacteriology, food poisoning, food storage, shopping and storage of food
Key Stage 4	Food safety, contamination and hazards, HACCP, cleaning and pest control

Science	Basic microbiology, detergents, temperature
Numeracy	Multiplication of bacteria, cooking times
Literacy	Reading cooking instructions
Food Technology	Use of catering equipment and safe use of ingredients
PSHE & Citizenship	Hand washing, disease prevention, personal hygiene
History	Food adulteration, effects of food poisoning and disease on populations and communities
Information Technology	Designing food hygiene posters

The students in secondary schools may then be able to go to do a Foundation Certificate in Food Hygiene. This will give them a qualification which they may be able to use for their first job application.

Key skills

By the time a student accesses continuing, further or higher education, the QCA will require details about how accredited certificate examinations will provide opportunities for demonstrating Key Skills. Key Skills are the generic skills which individuals need in order to be effective members of a flexible, adaptable and competitive workforce and for lifelong learning.
Key skills include:
♦ communication;
♦ application of numbers;
♦ information technology;
♦ problem-solving;
♦ improving own learning and performance; and.
♦ working with others.

Originally the government wanted to encourage more 16-19 year olds to develop their Key Skills to higher levels including those taking A levels. This led to the development of a Key Skills strategy. Key Skills build on the basic skills. They enable people to be competent and confident as they use these skills in a wide range of contexts and at higher levels, and to apply the key skills learned in one environment to meet new demands in another. The Key Skills home site is http://www.dfes.gov.uk/key/

OFSTED

The Office for Standards in Education (Ofsted) is a non-ministerial government department which seeks to improve the standards and quality of education and childcare through independent regulation and inspection. Ofsted's inspection roles are managed under the Education (Schools) Act 1992, and the Care Standards Act 2000. Where food is provided by establishments (schools, crèches, Under 8's groups, childminders, etc) for children to eat then inspectors may require food hygiene training for staff. Visit www.ofsted.gov.uk or use a local telephone directory to obtain more information.

Lastly...

Food hygiene education must start in the home and at school as food safety is the responsibility of both businesses and consumers. Behavioural change has to be monitored and changes in training strategies changed as necessary. Current food hygiene training is clearly not working. The whole population, whether working in a food business or not, need to be persuaded to produce high quality safe food at home and at work. Food hygiene training does have a place in the Government's Lifelong Learning programme which makes education and training accessible to all in the community from "cradle to the grave".

The face and nature of education and training across all levels and for all abilities in the UK is undergoing a major overhaul this century. There will be far more to taking a food hygiene certificate in the future, than, say, twenty years ago. A food hygiene certificate course can no longer be viewed as a food handler attending a 1, 2, 3 or 5 day course to improve food hygiene awareness. It will set the food handler up with basic and key skills. Mixed together all these skills and an increased knowledge of food hygiene will contribute to the individual's lifelong learning and development, which will provide them with motivation and greater job opportunities. For their employer it will mean a better educated, committed (and hopefully competent) employee. In turn all these factors will contribute to a better standard of public health and economic outlook.

The hospitality and food industries need to demonstrate, especially to small businesses, that learning cultures benefit both employers and employees. The employer needs help and guidance in setting up a culture. In addition, the employee will need to be shown links between learning and career progression. Opportunities for implementation and financial aid will also need to be explained. If any future courses are to be developed whether in-house, or subject to QCA accreditation, the content must be researched, studied and reviewed to ensure not only that it meets the needs of industry, but also that the course is suitable for the recipient.

In closing, effective and proven training solutions and practical implementation of systems such as hazard analysis need to be pressed home to businesses (and the enforcement officers who carry out the inspections) if there is to be any national tangible benefit from effective food hygiene training.

A Director of the Public Health Laboratory Service (PHLS) provides the last words which must not be forgotten when planning food hygiene training in the future. J Cruickshank had a paper published in the British Medical Journal (1990) in which he stated: "Good hygiene, both personal and food handling practices, is the basis for preventing the transmission of pathogens from food handling personnel to consumers..."

Appendix I Useful Contacts

Examples of useful contacts are given below. They may provide specialist advice and materials for trainers. Many of them have useful links to other sites which are worth exploring. The internet, with its range of search engines, has a wealth of food hygiene training information relevant to the hospitality and food retail industries. Examples of resource suppliers are given in this appendix. Try www.yell.com to look up suppliers of specific items, or the annual Caterer and Hotelkeeper directory of products, services and information at www.caterer.com

ASSOCIATIONS

NAME	TEL NUMBER	WEB SITE
Automatic Vending Association	020 8661 1112	www.ava-vending.org
British Hospitality Association	020 7404 7744	www.bha.org.uk
British Institute of Cleaning Science	01604 678710	www.bics.org
British Institute of Innkeeping	01276 417 838	www.bii.org.uk
British Pest Control Association	01332 294288	www.bpca.org.uk
British Sandwich Association	01235 821 820	www.sandwich.org.uk
Catering Managers Association of Great Britain and the Channel Islands	01947 895514	
Chartered Institute of Personnel and Development	020 8971 9000	www.cipd.co.uk
Greater London Seafish Group Training Association	020 7517 3545	www.seafoodtraining.org
Hospitality Network	020 8579 2400	www.hospitalitynetwork.org.uk
Hotel Catering and International Management Association	020 8772 7400	www.hcima.org.uk

NAME	TEL NUMBER	WEB SITE
Hotel and Catering Personnel and Training Association	020 7493 3212	www.hcpta.com
Ice Cream Alliance	0115 985 8505	www.ice-cream.org
Institute of Food Science and Technology	020 7603 6316	www.ifst.org
International Hotel and Restaurant Association	00 33 (0) 1 44 89 94 20	www.ih-ra.com
Institute of Training and Occupational Learning	0161 483 4577	www.itol.co.uk
Local Authorities Caterers' Association	01483 766777	www.laca.co.uk
Mobile and Outside Catering Association	0121 693 7000	www.moca.org.uk
Pizza and Pasta Association	01235 821 820	www.papa.org.uk
Restaurant Association	020 7831 8727	www.ragb.co.uk

Visit www.berkeley-scott.com/links_industry.htm for a list of hospitality organisations.

AWARDING EXAMINATION BODIES

The Chartered Institute of Environmental Health Chadwick Court, 15 Hatfields, London SE1 8DJ Telephone: 020 7928 6006	www.cieh.org.uk	Accredited examination body with the Qualification and Curriculum Authority. Offers food hygiene, health & safety and training skills qualifications. Has a Trainers' Charter. List of registered training centres.

The Royal Institute of Public Health 28 Portland Place, London, WC1N 4DE Telephone: 020 7580 2731	www.riph.org.uk	Accredited examination body with the Qualification and Curriculum Authority. Offers food hygiene and other qualifications. The Institute has a Certification of Training Packs service which covers any type of training pack/course/materials whose objective is to contribute to teaching aspects of health, hygiene and safety. List of registered training centres.
The Royal Society for the Promotion of Health 38a St Georges Drive, London SW1V 4BH Telephone: 020 7630 0121	www.rsph.org	Accredited examination body with the Qualification and Curriculum Authority. Offers food hygiene, health & safety and training skills qualifications. List of registered training centres.
The Royal Environmental Health Institute of Scotland 3 Manor Place, Edinburgh, EH3 7DH Telephone: 0131 225 6999	www.rehis.org	Accredited examination body with the Qualification and Curriculum Authority. Offers food hygiene, health & safety and training skills qualifications. List of registered training centres.
The Society of Food Hygiene Technology PO Box 37, Lymington, Hants, SO41 9WL Telephone: 01590 671979	www.sofht.co.uk	Examination body for food hygiene courses. List of registered training centres.

E LEARNING

NAME	TEL NUMBER	WEB SITE
Adult Learning Partnership	01373 462462	www.adultlearning partnership.co.uk
British Nutrition Foundation	020 7404 6504	www.nutrition.org.uk
Caterer and Hotelkeeper	020 8652 8307	www.caterer.com

NAME	TEL NUMBER	WEB SITE
Creative Learning Media	01458 254440	www.creativelearningmedia.com
Fast Train	01883 623839	www.fastrain.co.uk
Learn Purple	020 7836 6999	www.learnpurple.co.uk
learndirect	0800 100 900	www.learndirect-advice.co.uk
NAICE	0116 204 4200	www.naice.org.uk
National Grid for Learning	024 7641 6994	www.ngfl.gov.uk
National Learning Network	024 7641 6994	www.nln.ac.uk
QFT UK Ltd	01482 861040	www.qft.co.uk
Scottish Adult Learning Partnership	0800 100 900	www.salp.org.uk
University for Industry	0114 291 5000	www.ufiltd.co.uk
Virtual College		www.food.virtual-college.co.uk

EDUCATION AND QUALIFICATION ADVICE

NAME	WEB SITE	NOTES
Sector Skills Organisation		
Food and Drink Industry National Training Organisation	www.foodanddrinknto.org.uk	Industry body supplies advice on training and education to food and drinks companies.
Hospitality Training Foundation	www.htf.org.uk	Sector Skills Council for the hospitality industry. Formerly national training organisation. Provides details of recognised qualifications for the industry and publications. National Qualification framework as well as Modern Apprenticeships.
Accreditation Body		
Qualifications and Curriculum Authority	www.qca.org.uk	Accredits and monitors qualifications in schools, colleges and at work.

Other Awarding Bodies		
City and Guilds	www.city-and-guilds.co.uk	Provides craft skills and training qualifications.
Edexcel	www.edexcel.org.uk	Vocational qualifications, BTEC and other further education certificate courses.
FUNDING and SUPPORT		
Business Link	www.businesslink.org.uk	Development opportunities and funding advice for small businesses.
Learning and Skills Council	www.lsc.org.uk	Co-ordinates and funds post-16 education in further education colleges, sixth forms, work-based training and adult learning.
Training and Employment Agency	www.delni.gov.uk	Advice for businesses in Northern Ireland.
Learning Opportunities Advice		
National Institute of Adult Continuing Education	www.niace.org.uk	NIACE aims "to promote the study and general advancement of adult continuing education"
Adult Learning Inspectorate	www.ali.gov.uk	Provides information for specific industry training standards.
Learning and Skills Development Agency	www.lsda.org.uk	Information available about developing further education for post 16 year olds.
Modern Apprenticeships	www.dfes.gov.uk/mapintro.htm	Modern apprenticeship information.
learndirect	www.learndirect.co.uk	**learndirect** offers high quality learning at a time, place and pace to suit individuals.
Local authorities	Every local authority in the UK is listed at www.tagish.co.uk. The websites for local authorities start with www, followed by the name of the authority, followed by .gov.uk. For example: www.rbkc.gov.uk for the Royal Borough of Kensington and Chelsea or www.wakefield.gov.uk for Wakefield.	Local authorities have business support services, education and adult learning departments, environmental health departments, etc. The services may or may not be free.

NAME	WEB SITE	NOTES
Colleges of Further Education	Websites for colleges are written as, for example: www.kcc.ac.uk for Kensington and Chelsea College	
Adult Education Services	Websites for services are written as, for example: www.waes.ac.uk for Westminster Adult Education Service	
Higher education such as Universities	Websites for Universities are written as, for example: www.tvu.ac.uk for Thames Valley University	
Association of Learning Providers	www.cesi.org.uk/projects/ten/alp	The association of Learning Providers represent a major proportion of the UK's work-based learning providers.

FOOD SAFETY MANAGEMENT AND HACCP ADVICE

NAME	TEL NUMBER	WEB SITE
Her Majesty's Stationery Office	01603 723011	www.hmso.gov.uk
Food Standards Agency	0845 606 0667	www.food.gov.uk
US Government		www.nal.usda.gov
Salford University	0161 295 2021	www.e-haccp.org.uk
University of Wales Institute Cardiff	029 2041 6070	www.uwic.ac.uk
CCFRA	01386 842104	www.camden.co.uk
Highfield.co.uk Ltd	0845 2260350	www.highfield.co.uk
Support Training and Services plc	01252 728300	www.hygenico.co.uk

FURTHER READING MATERIALS

Business	Website
Basic Skills Agency	www.basic-skills.co.uk
Business Education Publishers Ltd	www.bepl.com
Butterworth-Heinemann	www.bh.com
Capstone Publishing	www.capstoneideas.com
Caterer and Hotelkeeper Magazine	www.caterer,com
Chartered Institute of Environmental Health	www.cieh.org.uk
Croners	www.croners.co.uk
Eaton Publications	www.eatonpubs.net
Gower	www.pubeasy.books.bookpoint.co.uk
Highfield.co.uk Ltd	www.highfield.co.uk
HMSO Publications	www.hmso.gov.uk
Hospitality Training Foundation	www.htf.org.uk
Institute of Food Science and Technology	www.ifst.org.uk
World Health Organisation	www.who.int

OTHER CONTACTS

Australia Food Standards Authority	www.foodstandards.gov.au
Canadian Food Standards Authority	www.cfis.agr.ca/english
EduCater	www.educater.ie
European Food Standards Authority	www.efsa.eu.int
Finding a trainer	www.foodsafetytrainers.co.uk
Floodlight guides to courses	www.floodlight.co.uk
Food Standards Agency	www.foodsafety.gov
Food Standards Authority of Ireland	www.fsai.ie
Foodforum	www.foodforum.org.uk
foodlink	www.foodlink.org.uk
International Food Information Service	www.ifis.org
Key Skills Home Site	www.dfes.gov.uk/key
Kogan Page Publishers	www.kogan-page.co.uk
Local Authorities Coordinators of Regulatory Services	www.lacors.gov.uk
New Zealand Food Standards Authority	www.foodstandards.govt.nz

NW London Food Club	www.thefoodclub.org.uk
Seafish Training Company	www.seafish.co.uk
The Royal Borough of Kensington & Chelsea	www.rbkc.org.uk/foodhygienestandards
Try a search engine	www.splut.com **or** www.google.co.uk
US Government Departments	www.fsis.usda.gov
USA Food Safety Training Education Alliance	www.fstea.org
USA Government Food Safety Educators Network	www.ednet-l@foodsafety.gov
Wellcome Library Information Service	wisdom.wellcome.ac.uk/resources

SPECIAL NEEDS AND LEARNING DIFFICULTIES

Adult Education Services	See yellow Pages (www.yell.com) or your local telephone directory
British Dyslexia Association	www.bda-dyslexia.org.uk
Basic Skills Agency	www.basic-skills.co.uk
Basic Skills Resource Centre	www.ioe.ac.uk/library/bsa
Campaign Against Age Discrimination in Employment	www.caade.net
Disability Rights Commission	www.drc-gb.org
Dyslexia Institute	www.dyslexia-inst.org.uk
Employers Forum on Disability	www.employers-forum.co.uk
Highfield.co.uk Ltd	www.highfield.co.uk
MIND	www.mind.org.uk
Plain English Campaign	www.plainenglish.co.uk
RNIB	www.rnib.org.uk
RNID	www.rnid.org.uk
Social Services	www2.tagish.co.uk
Special Needs Services	www.theteachernetwork.com/special
Wigan and Leigh College	www.wigan-leigh.ac.uk

VIDEOS

British Meat Education	www.bmesonline.org.uk
British Nutrition Foundation	www.nutrition.org.uk
Classroom videos	www.classroomvideo.com

Eaton Publications	www.eatonpubs.net
Educater	www.educater.ie
Food Forum Videos	www.foodforum.org.uk
Highfield.co.uk Ltd	www.highfield.co.uk
Videotel	www.videotel.com

COMMUNITY LANGUAGES

The examination bodies, local authorities, community groups and many other organisations may be able to give assistance in providing contact names and addresses of potential community trainers who may be registered to run accredited or non- accredited food hygiene courses in languages other than English. The lists shown here may well be out of date depending upon the movements of the trainers. Check with the various examination bodies. Various translation services and free translations are available on the internet.

The Royal Institute of Public Health

The Royal Institute of Public Health has a directory of trainers able to speak different languages. Many of the trainers work for companies and only provide in-house training, so the list of available trainers and languages will be considerably smaller than this. The Royal Institute of Public Health examinations are normally written in English. The trainer is responsible for translating the answers back to English. Tests may be held in another language when requested. In the case of candidates being unable to understand the written paper a scribe or interpreter may be arranged.

The list of language trainers is as follows:

Afrikaans	Finnish	Krio (Pidgin)	Punjabi	Thai
Arabic	French	Maltese	Putonghua	Turkish
Basque	German	Mandarin	Russian	Urdu
Cantonese	Greek	Mirpuri	Sign language	Welsh
Chinese	Hebrew	Persian	Spanish	Yoruba
Dutch	Hokkien	Polish	Swedish	Zulu
Farsi	Hungarian	Portuguese	Teochew	

Enquirers are requested to contact The Royal Institute of Public Health on 020 7580 2731 or e-mail: info@riph.org.uk for further information.

The Chartered Institute of Environmental Health

Enquirers are asked to contact Centre Support at The Chartered Institute of Environmental Health on 020 7928 6006 for details of their nearest registered language trainers.

Arabic	Cantonese	Farsi	Greek	Hindi
Bengali	Dutch	French	Gujarati	Italian

The Chartered Institute of Environmental Health offer examinations (and * work books) in the following languages:

Kurdish	Punjabi	Somali	Turkish	
Mandarin	Spanish	Tamil	Urdu	

If you are in any doubt contact www.cieh.org.uk.

Bengali*	French*	Hindi	Spanish*	Welsh*
Cantonese*	Hindi	Italian*	Thai	
Croatian	German*	Portuguese*	Turkish	
Dutch	Gujarati*	Punjabi	Urdu	

The Royal Society for the Promotion of Health

Papers are available in English. Enquirers are advised to contact The Royal Society for the Promotion of Health for further information. Telephone 020 630 0121 or visit www.rshealth.org

Asian and Oriental School of Catering

Food hygiene courses and advice available in a wide range of Asian and Oriental languages (including Thai, Vietnamese, Japanese, Indian sub-Continent languages). Translation service. Telephone 020 7613 9292. Visit www.spice-train.com.

Highfield.co.uk Limited

Highfield offers books, videos, posters & notices as training materials in a number of foreign languages. e-Learning and CBT products are also available.

Appendix II Food Poisoning
& Its Place in Food Hygiene Training

"You won't be surprised that diseases are innumerable – count the cooks." Seneca c.4 BC-AD 65

The Advisory Committee on the Microbiological Safety of Food in 1992 defined food poisoning as: any disease of an infectious or toxic nature caused by or thought to be caused by consumption of food or water. Food poisoning as a term is widely used in public health legislation. It is also commonly used for level 1 food hygiene courses. Government, enforcement agencies, and the health services generally accept the term Foodborne Illness. It is introduced in level 2 and 3 syllabuses. To avoid confusion amongst candidates one of the terms ought to be used throughout accredited food hygiene syllabuses, whichever term is used by examination bodies it ought to be consistent with that used by the Government, Agencies, and the health services.

Food hygiene training, properly managed, implemented and legislated, provides a lifelong skill which needs to involve the whole UK population. Food poisoning prevention is the result of ignorance, misconceptions, woolly legislation, and diverse interpretations. Living in a society where apportioning blame, but not admitting guilt or responsibility, is becoming increasingly common. These may do food hygiene training programmes more harm than good.

Ask trainees at the start of a food hygiene course about their knowledge of food poisoning and the answers may be various. A question such as "Why are you really here?" will reveal a mixture of answers too. A good trainer will try to allay some misconceptions about food poisoning. Trainees may be advised as follows:

♦ to understand that law enforcement is not sufficient to prevent food poisoning;
♦ to learn not to point the finger of blame at hotel and catering businesses as soon as an individual or others feel ill after eating something;
♦ to understand that the majority of businesses do their best to serve safe food and do not want to lose their customers through bad publicity and legal action;
♦ to improve an individual's food hygiene standards at home *as well as* at work;
♦ to change an individual's current food hygiene practices which may be putting their family, friends, colleagues, clients, patients and/or customers at risk;
♦ to appreciate the essentials of good food hygiene practice;
♦ it is a catalogue of errors which contribute to a food poisoning incident – not just a one-off incident;
♦ food poisoning does not happen every day;
♦ there is more chance of it going right than going wrong;
♦ food poisoning is entirely preventable …using hazard analysis principles; and
♦ holding a certificate can provide a false sense of security. You will need to demonstrate that you can practise good food hygiene standards all the time.

The confusion over use of statistics, terminology, and causes of food poisoning needs to be cleared up if trainers, managers, employees and the public are to have a better understanding about the reality of food poisoning in the UK. Everyone needs to sing from the same hymn sheet and be taught about what needs to be achieved to produce a real reduction in food poisoning.

Appendix III Is Your Menu Safe?

A proposal for a Regulation of the European parliament and the Council on the hygiene of foodstuffs (2000/C 365 E/02) which was submitted to the European Commission on 14 July 2000 gave a definition for food safety which will affect all EU member states once the Regulation is implemented. The definition reads "...the assurance that food will not cause adverse health effects to the final consumer when it is prepared and eaten taking into account its intended use." The EU proposal does not place any more emphasis on the duties and responsibilities of food business owners with regards to food safety and food hygiene.

Have a look at some of the commonly used ingredients below:
- cooked meats and poultry;
- cooked meat products (gravy, stock, pâté, etc);
- milk, cream, artificial cream, custards and dairy produce;
- cooked eggs and products made with fresh shelled eggs (mayonnaise, tiramisu, meringues, etc);
- shellfish (mussels, oysters, etc) and other seafoods;
- cooked rice; and
- salads, vegetables and fruit that need no further preparation.

The ingredients require:
- strict temperature control (i.e. on delivery, correct freezing, thawing, refrigeration, cooking, display and service);
- protection from germs (bacteria, viruses, etc), chemicals (cleaning chemicals, disinfectants, sanitisers, food additives), and anything likely to injure or harm your customers or employees. (Protection starts with the producers, your suppliers through to all stages in your business.)

How will a manager of a food business know that…
- *Salmonella, Clostridium perfringens, E. coli, Bacillus cereus, Staphylococcus aureus, Listeria monocytogenese*;
- poisons in tuna, mackerel, sardines, pilchards, herring, anchovies and salmon;
- peanuts, walnuts, almonds, brazil nuts, hazelnuts, pistachio, shellfish, and sesame seeds (and other foods likely to cause an allergic reaction, including oils used in dressings or for cooking);
- cleaning chemicals, disinfectants, excess food additives and preservatives; and
- hair, glass, metal, packaging, nails and other physical items

…are not in the delivered ingredients or have not got into the ingredients at any stage of their business? None of the ingredients listed above are particularly new. The theory of food safety and its role in the use of the menu items have been known for some time.

Ignorance and a lack of application of food hygiene and food safety principles, practices, and compliance with current legislation increase the chances of businesses losing their customers through illness or reputation, and may even face prosecution or civil action, and higher insurance premiums. Is avoiding food hygiene management responsibilities really worth the risk? It is important to be able to demonstrate an understanding of:

 ♦ preparing and implementing a hazard analysis;
 ♦ ensuring management and staff have received suitable food hygiene training (including induction and refresher). Not just attending courses, but putting theory into practice;
 ♦ developing a food safety culture;
 ♦ the importance of time temperature control;
 ♦ the need to follow suppliers' instructions concerning storage, chilling, freezing, thawing, cooking, stock rotation, etc;
 ♦ the purpose of cleaning chemicals and disinfectants; and
 ♦ the requirements of food safety legislation.

The role of managers and supervisors is key to menu and ingredient safety. Supervision, instruction, practical implementation of theory taught on courses, monitoring, reviewing standards, and involvement of employees are vital.

Appendix IV HACCP and Training

"Knowing is not enough; we must apply. Willing is not enough; we must do." (Goethe 1749-1832)

In common with food hygiene, HACCP (Hazard Analysis Critical Control Point) is a 24-hour business. It is not something that is put on when arriving at work, and taken off when clocking off. Food handlers and their managers need to be taught that any food safety management system such as Hazard Analysis and HACCP require nurturing and looking after over a 24 hour period.

A commonly asked question by managers of food businesses is "how often should my staff receive refresher training?" or, "how will I know if my staff have the right level of training?" The answer at first glance is relatively simple. If a hazard analysis is properly carried out, implemented, and monitored then the answer will be straightforward. Managers have difficulty complying with the legislation because they have insufficient food hygiene knowledge, or they are misled into thinking that this whole process is rocket science adapted for food production plants.

There are innumerable publications about HACCP and other food safety management systems. Many of them are complex and can cause confusion unless the reader has a good grasp of food safety. Refer to the bibliography at the end of this book. Reading is one form of training – so long as the knowledge gained is put into practice and assessed.

Producing pages of technical information as a documented system is not training. Something has to be done with the documents. Managers may fall into the trap of inadvertently testing literacy, language and food hygiene skills of their employees. If this happens systems will fail. Often overlooked is the fact that terminology used in HACCP is in English. Translations into other languages do present problems – not just international, but also nearer to home in the EU member states.

Team building and joint working on a food safety management issue will give everyone concerned a sense of involvement and an understanding of their responsibilities within the organisation.

Consultants may be asked by businesses to produce documented systems. But as small and large businesses have found to their cost, some of these consultants who consider themselves experts in HACCP and food safety management systems are more expert in taking money and leaving behind confusion. Take the example of a large chain of café restaurants. A consultant was employed to produce a generic documented system. A glossy A4 lever arch file full of forms and instructions was sent to all 197 businesses in the UK. Not one word of training was given to the manager of staff in each unit. The manager was expected to complete the forms and show them to the visiting EHO. Systems failed and customers fell ill. On the other hand, there are some very good consultants who spend time and effort with all levels of employees going through a plan that will suit that particular business. Pre-course and post-training evaluations are carried out to ensure everyone knows what their role is and that the systems work. If they do not then appropriate remedial action is taken.

Local authority food safety enforcement officers and EHOs are currently not required to carry out a Hazard Analysis for businesses. The majority of local authorities do not have the resources to do this. There are a few who do see education as a legitimate part of the enforcement process. Some will produce Hazard Analysis templates for businesses, such as the

Wyre Borough Council and the Royal Borough of Kensington and Chelsea are two that do so. Others have food safety forums and attend food clubs (such as the Food Club in NW London). These foster good relationships and encourage self-empowerment. When HACCP hits the high streets local authorities would benefit from ring-fenced funding to employ HACCP trainers for small businesses. These trainers would then go into a business to give practical guidance following a visit from an enforcement officer. The other advantage is that the local authority and its food businesses would build up a meaningful relationship – one which the media all too often trying to dismantle by press articles and television programmes entitled "Restaurants from Hell" or "The Food Police".

Computer based training may be an answer to hazard analysis and HACCP. Any package produced will have to suit the needs of particular types and sizes of businesses. Standard forms, as part of the programme, may help the candidates but the question arises about who is going to verify and monitor the implementation?

Classroom based courses have a place too. Few exist. The examination bodies such as CIEH, RSPH and RIPH all have certificate courses but even these do not attract many of the types of managers that are to shortly be affected by the changes in legislation. Although, as indicated above, HACCP training for managers is to become a mandatory requirement, it will only be effective if managers receive management and leadership skills along with support in turning classroom based theory into practice. A certificate will, like current food hygiene certificate courses, not be a test of competence. To coin a saying: "the proof of the pudding will be in the eating" – but at what cost or whose expense?!

Trainers, enforcers, government agencies, businesses and consultants are encouraged to broaden their horizons. The World Wide Web provides an invaluable training resource for HACCP and how it can be adapted to suit the needs of all types of businesses. The UK is years behind in producing free accessible information. Many of the sites are interactive and downloadable. There are forms, examples, on-line certificate courses, links to other advice sources, and more. The following links are just a few examples. But first of all visit www.food.gov.uk and have a look at what exists in the UK. This site is run by the Food Standards Agency. Compare it to a site such as www.rbkc.gov.uk/foodhygieneandstandards, or any of the others which can be found just by typing in key words such as "HACCP training, hazard analysis for managers", etc. food**link**, in 2002, launched a food safety communication awards scheme as a means to encourage local authorities and eventually businesses to promote food safety. How long will it be before there is a HACCP "made easy" award scheme?

The Food Standards Agency:	No information about hazard analysis training or food safety management systems. Some advice relating to butchers shops about HACCP.
The Royal Borough of Kensington and Chelsea	Hazard analysis flow chart, hazard analysis made easy, food safety pack, food hygiene training, common food safety failures of management. HACCP not introduced yet.
Caterer and Hotelkeeper	The trade magazine have produced a web site. The information is of limited use. Visit www.caterer.com

The problem with training in the UK, whether it is on the web or in print, is that there is very little food safety information in other languages. The lead from the Food Standards Agency at present is minimal. In a multi-cultural society this is unacceptable. Eaton Publications does produce a limited amount and Highfield.co.uk Ltd have products translated into twenty different languages, including books, posters and videos. But there are many food handlers who have literacy difficulties with their own mother tongue. Highfield.co.uk Ltd and Creative Learning Media also provide multimedia software programmes in Spanish, Portuguese and German. Various consultancy firms do offer advice and training. Ensure that your staff are made to feel part of the solution and not part of the problem. Challenge the consultants – ask them for references, case studies and how they will involve employees in the business when putting a food safety management system together. Be careful with distance learning HACCP training programmes. Too many leave trainees with a theoretical knowledge, but post-course the trainees are in no better position to apply the knowledge in an accurate and meaningful way than they were beforehand. Go overseas and the reader will find that the UK is easily put to shame.

America	America has a staggering collection of advice about HACCP and food safety training. It is free to use and user friendly. As a training tool however the difficulty for businesses is to ensure that what they have learnt works in practice. The effectiveness is yet to be judged. Try, for example: Food Safety Training Education Alliance www.fstea.org Food Protection www.foodprotection.org US Government www.fsis.usda.gov
Australia	Visit www.dfst.csiro.au. There is even more information available if the health departments of separate states are visited.
Canada	There is a web site produced in partnership between the government and the food industry: www.canfightbac.org
Ireland	The Food Standards Authority of Ireland produces clear guidance about training and HACCP. The Authority has carried out surveys to establish the understanding of HACCP in small businesses. Like the UK, it is clear that there is a long way to go before all food businesses are able to make proper use of HACCP to benefit their specific types of business. Visit www.fsai.ie

Look elsewhere
Finally

HACCP makes sense. Information about HACCP should be improved and training must focus on changing behaviour of both managers and food handlers. As a system it will only be as effective as the competency of the people using the process. But the skills to train others to apply practical knowledge in a meaningful way for a wide range of businesses is sadly lacking. It is a comprehensive means to taking in a wide range of ingredients, processes and later use of products. HACCP is unceasing and by nature is a step by step thorough plan covering operations and procedures. Enforcement agencies and EHOs needed to be aware of the

Definitions

The definitions used in this section may differ from those in the main text of the book. This demonstrates the diversity of definitions, whether on the statute books, in industry guides and codes of practice, or used in everyday life by the general public.

AGEISM	Discrimination of individuals on grounds of their age
ATTITUDE	A feeling regarding something
BASIC SKILLS	The ability to read, write and speak in English and use mathematics at a level necessary to function and progress at work and in society in general
BEHAVIOURAL CHANGE	The way an individual reacts or works after education and training
CANDIDATE	Someone studying for and taking a examination
CERTIFICATION	Written declaration
CLASSROOM-BASED TRAINING	Training which takes place in a room designed for training a group of individuals
CODE OF PRACTICE	Legal guidance concerning the statutory implementation and interpretation of an act or regulation
COGNITIVE	Acquisition of knowledge
COMMENSURATE	Proportionate to a specific job or position
COMPETENCE	Ability or efficiency
CULTURE	The way in which something is performed or how people work
DEVELOPMENT	Improvement
DUE DILIGENCE	Adequate care
DYSLEXIA	Difficulty in learning to read words, letters and symbols
EDUCATION	Cultivation of the mind
E-LEARNING	Electronic learning
EVALUATION	Careful assessment
FOOD	Any substance consumed to support life, including ice and drink
FOOD BORNE DISEASE	Illness resulting in the consumption of food contaminated by pathogenic microorganisms and/or their toxins
FOOD BUSINESS	Any business in the course of which commercial operations with regard to food, or food sources, are carried out (whether for profit or not)

FOOD HANDLER	Any person in a food business who handles food, whether open or packaged (food includes ice and drink)
FOOD HANDLING	Any operation in the production, preparation, processing, packaging, storage, transport, distribution and sale of food
FOOD HYGIENE	All measures deemed necessary to ensure the safety and wholesomeness of food during preparation, processing, manufacture, storage, transportation, distribution, handling and offering for sale or supply to the consumer
FOOD INDUSTRY	A business which mass produces food for wholesale or retail purposes
FOOD POISONING	An acute illness of sudden onset caused by the recent consumption of contaminated or poisonous food
FOOD PREMISES	Any premises where food is stored, prepared, cooked or served for consumption by customers or charges, employees
FOOD STANDARDS	Nature, substance or quality of food which is to be consumed
HACCP	A scienced based food safety management system for systematically identifying hazards and risks of food production and the implementation of cost-effective controls and monitoring procedures at points critical to food safety
HAZARD	Something with the potential to cause harm
HAZARD ANALYSIS	A system which enables a food business to identify hazards, the steps in the operation at which they may occur, and the introduction of measures to reduce them to a safe level or remove them altogether
HOSPITALITY INDUSTRY	Usually includes pubs, clubs, wine bars, leisure clubs, cafés, take-aways, hotels, restaurants, institutional and health service catering
HYGIENE	The science of preserving health and involves all measures necessary to improve the safety and wholesomeness of food
IMPLEMENTATION	Putting into action
INDUCTION	Informing about basic key points for the performance of an operation
INDUSTRY GUIDE	Advice to food business on how to comply with the Food Safety (General Food Hygiene) Regulations 1995

IN-HOUSE TRAINING	Training which takes place within a food premises rather than at a college or consultants' premises
INSTRUCTION	Teaching or an authoritive order on how to use or operate something
KEY SKILLS	Essential skills which people need in order to be effective members of a flexible, adaptable and competitive workforce
KNOWLEDGE	Everything that is understood
LEARNING	Skill or knowledge that has been gained by study
LESSON	A period of instruction
LITERACY	The ability to read and write
MANAGER	A person who is in the control of a business or department or specific operation
MOTIVATION	Provision of an incentive
PROPRIETOR	An owner of a business
RESOURCE	An available means of support or assistance, in terms or materials, people, and money
SPECIAL NEEDS	Specific help required for well-being and participation in both social and business communities due to disability, impairment, basic skill deficiency, language difficulties, etc.
STRATEGY	The art of planning or managing the way something is to be performed
STUDENT	Any person who undertakes study
SUPERVISOR	A person who is in charge
TEACHING	Imparting knowledge
TRAINEE	An individual who is being trained to perform a specific task
TRAINING	Bringing of an individual up to a desired level or proficient standard
UNDERSTANDING	Knowing something thoroughly

Abbreviations

Commonly used abbreviations in Effective Food Hygiene Training

AFH	ADVANCED CERTIFICATE IN FOOD HYGIENE
ALI	ADULT LEARNING INSPECTORATE
AMA	ADVANCED MODERN APPRENTICESHIP
AVA	AUDIO VISUAL AIDS
BDA	BRITISH DYSLEXIA ASSOCIATION
BHA	BRITISH HOSPITALITY ASSOCIATION
BII	BRITISH INSTITUTE OF INN KEEPING
BNF	BRITISH NUTRITION FOUNDATION
BPCA	BRITISH PEST CONTROL ASSOCIATION
BS	BRITISH STANDARD
BSA	BASIC SKILLS AGENCY
CBT	COMPUTER BASED TRAINING
CDSC	COMMUNICABLE DISEASE SURVEILLANCE CENTRE
CHGL	CHADWICK HOUSE GROUP LTD
CIEH	CHARTERED INSTITUTE OF ENVIRONMENTAL HEALTH
CIPD	CHARTERED INSTITUTE OF PERSONNEL AND DEVELOPMENT
CLM	CREATIVE LEARNING MEDIA
COP	CODE OF PRACTICE
DFES	DEPARTMENT FOR EDUCATION AND SKILLS
DOH	DEPARTMENT OF HEALTH
EFSA	EUROPEAN FOOD SAFETY AUTHORITY
EHO	ENVIRONMENTAL HEALTH OFFICER
ESF	EUROPEAN SOCIAL FUND
ESOL	ENGLISH FOR SPEAKERS OF OTHER LANGUAGES
EU	EUROPEAN UNION
FAO	FOOD AND AGRICULTURE ORGANISATION
FCFH	FOUNDATION CERTIFICATE IN FOOD HYGIENE
FDA	FOOD AND DRUGS ADMINISTRATION
FDF	FOOD AND DRINKS FEDERATION
FE	FURTHER EDUCATION
FMA	FOUNDATION IN MODERN APPRENTICESHIP
FSA	FOOD STANDARDS AGENCY
FSAI	FOOD STANDARDS AUTHORITY OF IRELAND
FSTEA	FOOD SAFETY TRAINING EDUCATION ALLIANCE
GCSE	GENERAL CERTIFICATE OF SECONDARY EDUCATION
GNVQ	GENERAL NATIONAL VOCATIONAL QUALIFICATION
GOV	GOVERNMENT
HA	HAZARD ANALYSIS
HACCP	HAZARD ANALYSIS CRITICAL CONTROL POINT
HCIMA	HOTEL CATERING AND INTERNATIONAL MANAGEMENT ASSOCIATION
HCTC	HOTEL AND CATERING TRAINING COMPANY
HDA	HEALTH DEVELOPMENT AGENCY

HE	HIGHER EDUCATION
HMSO	HER MAJESTY'S STATIONERY OFFICE
HTF	HOSPITALITY TRAINING FOUNDATION
IFH	INTERMEDIATE CERTIFICATE IN FOOD HYGIENE
IFIS	INTERNATIONAL FOOD INFORMATION SERVICE
IID	INTESTINAL INFECTIOUS DISEASE
IIP	INVESTORS IN PEOPLE
INT	INTERNATIONAL
IPM	INSTITUTE OF PERSONNEL MANAGEMENT
ISO	INTERNATIONAL STANDARDS ORGANISATION
IT	INFORMATION TECHNOLOGY
ITOL	INSTITUTE OF TRAINING AND OCCUPATIONAL LEARNING
LACORS	LOCAL AUTHORITIES COORDINATORS OF REGULATORY SERVICES
LEC	LEARNING ENTERPRISE COMPANY
LSC	LEARNING AND SKILLS COUNCIL
LSDA	LEARNING AND SKILLS DEVELOPMENT AGENCY
LVSTC	LONDON VOLUNTARY SECTOR TRAINING CONSORTIUM
NCVQ	NATIONAL COUNCIL FOR VOCATIONAL QUALIFICATIONS
NEBSM	NATIONAL EXAMINATION BOARD FOR SUPERVISORY MANAGEMENT
NGFL	NATIONAL GRID FOR LEARNING
NHS	NATIONAL HEALTH SERVICE
NIACE	NATIONAL INSTITUTE FOR ADULT CONTINUING EDUCATION
NLP	NEURO LINGUISTIC PROGRAMMING
NTA	NATIONAL TRAINING AWARD
NTO	NATIONAL TRAINING ORGANISATION
NVQ	NATIONAL VOCATIONAL QUALIFICATION
PCT	PRIMARY CARE TRUST
PHLS	PUBLIC HEALTH LABORATORY SERVICE
QA	QUALITY ASSURANCE
QCA	QUALIFICATIONS AND CURRICULUM AUTHORITY
RA	RISK ASSESSMENT
REHIS	ROYAL ENVIRONMENTAL HEALTH INSTITUTE OF SCOTLAND
RIPH	ROYAL INSTITUTE OF PUBLIC HEALTH
RSPH	ROYAL SOCIETY FOR THE PROMOTION OF HEALTH
SOFHT	SOCIETY OF FOOD HYGIENE TECHNOLOGY
SSO	SECTOR SKILLS ORGANISATION
SVQ	SCOTTISH VOCATIONAL QUALIFICATION
TNA	TRAINING NEEDS ANALYSIS
UFI	UNIVERSITY FOR INDUSTRY
UK	UNITED KINGDOM
USA	UNITED STATE OF AMERICA
WHO	WORLD HEALTH ORGANISATION
WWW	WORLD WIDE WEB

Index